The Children of Shallowford

Other books by Henry Williamson

The Flax of Dream, the story of Willie Maddison, comprising four separate volumes:

THE BEAUTIFUL YEARS
DANDELION DAYS
THE DREAM OF FAIR WOMEN
THE PATHWAY
(Faber and Faber)

A Chronicle of Ancient Sunlight:

THE DARK LANTERN
DONKEY BOY
YOUNG PHILLIP MADDISON
HOW DEAR IS LIFE
A FOX UNDER MY CLOAK
THE GOLDEN VIRGIN
LOVE AND THE LOVELESS
A TEST TO DESTRUCTION
THE INNOCENT MOON
IT WAS THE NIGHTINGALE
THE POWER OF THE DEAD
THE PHOENIX GENERATION
A SOLITARY WAR
LUCIFER BEFORE SUNRISE
THE GALE OF THE WORLD
(Macdonald and Jane's)

Other Novels

THE STAR-BORN
THE GOLD FALCON
(Faber and Faber)

Country Books

LIFE IN A DEVON VILLAGE
TALES OF A DEVON VILLAGE
SALAR THE SALMON
THE PHASIAN BIRD
THE STORY OF A NORFOLK FARM
SCRIBBLING LARK
(Faber and Faber)
A CLEAR WATER STREAM
(Macdonald and Jane's)

Nature Books

THE LONE SWALLOWS
THE PEREGRINE'S SAGA, and other Wild Tales
THE OLD STAG, and other Hunting Stories
TARKA THE OTTER
(The Bodley Head)
THE HENRY WILLIAMSON ANIMAL SAGA
COLLECTED NATURE STORIES
THE SCANDAROON
(Macdonald and Jane's)

The Children of Shallowford

HENRY WILLIAMSON

MACDONALD AND JANE'S · LONDON

First published in 1939
by Faber and Faber Limited
Reissued in a new and revised edition,
with additional scenes, in 1959
by Faber and Faber Limited

This edition, with illustrations,
and an Afterword by Richard Williamson,
published in 1978 by
Macdonald and Jane's Publishers Limited
Paulton House
8 Shepherdess Walk
London, N1 7LW

ISBN 0 354 04313 7

Made and printed in Great Britain by
Billing and Sons Limited
London, Guildford and Worcester

Contents

To
MERIEL NORTH

Illustrations

Between pages 128 and 129

All the photographs were very kindly supplied by Richard Williamson and the Estate of Henry Williamson

I

Mother and Son

When our first child was born Loetitia and I had been married less than a year. During that time our life together had not always been easy, partly due to causes which went back to childhood, partly to differences in mind and nature. Loetitia was serene, having been overset by neither parent: indeed, she had been brought up by a nanny. Also she was not quickly imaginative; whereas I was too often agitated, because vividly imaginative. She got things done by patience; I achieved in nervous bursts, although in my eccentric way I was tenacious, even enduring. The early twenties was a difficult period, in which the ideas of the pre-1914 age were breaking down, with material change consequent. I was a rebel against things as they were; Loetitia accepted things as they were, asking only to be allowed to work long and selflessly for others. My mind, or nervous temperament, aggravated by meditations arising from a youth partly spent upon battle-fields, was striving always to dissolve the crystallized thought of the pre-war minded about me. My life was a dream of a world fairer than any I had known.

Of course I had to learn that, before the world can be

put in order, a man must put himself in order! Having stated this, I can get down to my account of our not infrequent happy moments of early married life, which begins just before we moved from a village in north Devon to an inland valley, to live in a thatched cottage beside the River Bray which ran down from Exmoor on its way to the sea of what is called Barnstaple Bay in Barnstaple and Bideford Bay in Bideford. It was a country of legend, in both fact and fiction; here, past the dreaded sand-bars at the mouth of the Two Rivers' estuary had come Hubba the Dane, the black raven pennants flying from his longships, to burn and pillage and be killed at Bloody Corner; and later, upon the conjoined ebb-tides sailed the frigates of Queen Elizabeth the First to join Drake's fleet gathering at Plymouth, to defeat, with the aid of the south-west gales which rage upon the coast, the galleons of the Spanish Armada.

Later came literature, celebrating the event in *Westward Ho!* by Charles Kingsley; and another romance, *Lorna Doone*, also by a local parson. I had ambitions to add to the literary associations of the rivers by writing a book about the wanderings of an otter. While I was getting local facts for the book, I kept a journal; and when the first baby was beginning to crawl entries concerning the little world of mother and child replaced those on the water-beast made when I was a bachelor.

Quietly happy in her new world of motherhood, Loetitia would sit knitting or sewing, while her little boy played in a pen on the nursery floor. His few toys were in a wooden box, which she had bought for a penny from the village shop. Each toy glowed for the mother with a life of its own, for her child. Bits of coloured paper—a catalogue of boys' railway trains—a ball—a wooden dog

—a large sunset-coloured sea-shell—these were the visible treasures of their world. She was always watching him, not with possessive directness, but as a shepherd on the downs grazes his flock. She knew his every movement: how he sat down for a moment, then climbed up to play awhile with the beads on the rail of his pen. While he was doing this, he might espy the bright hinge at the corner, and move himself around, by side-steps of half-unsocked feet and handclasps, until he got to the opposite side, holding meanwhile so carefully to the top rail.

Next, he sees something on the bookcase—a wooden bobbin. Standing on toes now free of sock, he grasps the bobbin, and slowly sits himself down, and is nearly down when he sees something more attractive—a large yellow sock Loetitia has just darned, by special request, with scarlet wool, to combine goldfinch colours. Up, again, and with the bobbin firmly grasped in the left hand, and holding the rail with the right, the baby tries to take the gaudy thing. Does he connect it with what he has seen on da-da's feet? He pulls it off the shelf, and it falls to the ground. Down he sits carefully, but finishes with a little bump.

Now the collection gotten with such effort, and thereby prized, must be examined; but even as he sits down his eye catches a piece of ribbon in a box, and this must be pulled at once. It tinkles, having a bell tied to it. While shaking this violently—hands and legs working together—his foot strikes a tin, in which is a halfpenny for a rattle. Immediately his heel goes bang-bang! on it, and he bangs and shakes so energetically that his mother fears he may over-balance. But he does not. And now a twist, a wriggle, a shuffle, and somehow he is back in front of the pen.

Loetitia seldom talks to him, she knows he plays more contentedly if left alone. How happy she is, sitting there by the pen, knitting a sock for him! Sometimes he catches her eye, and then the two laugh together, and he goes back happily to his toys—the beads, the box of treasures. But he sees something that excites him—red socks moving into the room round the half-open door, through which, unseen so far, an eye has been watching him, above red socks which have been darned, by special request, with yellow wool. 'Dad-dad!' as the socks come close to the pen. It is a game that the baby shall touch, through the bars of the pen, first one coloured sock, then the other, with a finger, before looking up at the face above him.

Loetitia is smiling with pleasure, for now there seems full happiness in the house. The wearer of bright socks—made specially on Loetitia's own new machine—pulls faces, sings, whistles and dances.

'Windles, shake hands!'—and out goes a small hand, which is gravely shaken, but held a moment too long, for it is snatched back. It is tried again, and this time the small hand is dropped at once. That is better—'I say, I've found out what it is—one must drop his hand at once, then he doesn't feel in prison.' Momentary wisdom, often lost in non-detachment; but the mother's face colours with pleasure, that father and son are happy together.

The double explodent of *Dad-dad* was one of the first definite sounds the baby uttered after he began to manage his own movements. Actually the first recognizable sound was *oo-la*, *oo-la*, the food cry which, to my past sorrow (but never exasperation) had usually changed to wails, then to screams of starvation, throughout the long nights when I had nursed him, while his mother lay upstairs in fever. After some weeks *oo-la* gave way to *num-num*, the food-cry of a healthy child; but *Dad-dad* was the baby developing and practising lip-and-mouth awareness with his sense of hearing. Also, it seemed that it came with the growth of the baby's first tooth, an irritation to be champed. The maternal nature, in wifely pride and gratitude, awarded this first distinctly uttered sound to the father. Would I, with innumerable other fathers, be known as Dappy or Coggy if a baby's first egocentric utterance were *Dap-dap* or *Cog-cog?*

Nevertheless, it was now too late to disclaim, with a purist's obstinacy, the baby's early recognition of my part in his being; for the very next morning, as Loetitia was putting him in his cot situate in a room with a very low lintel, known to my six-foot-tall self as Skullcracker (later it was hung with a row of coloured beads threaded on string through short lengths of straw), suddenly he gave a shout—Dad-dad! and all because my unshaven and somewhat cadaverous face had appeared round the door.

Although so often I failed to emulate their natural and therefore true ways, I knew that wild animals and birds owed their very life-forms to habit. At the same evening moment the white owl sailed from the dark opening in the gable end of the first cottage wherein Loetitia and I had come together to live. The owl flew silently over the tombstones and through the elms and over the tall hedge to the mice-runs in the grass of the glebe field. The owl knew its time by the sun. Migrant birds knew their times, too; and many, I thought, travelled by star-prints inherited in their minds. During my walks over the stubble-fields I saw the paths of rabbits and rats, with their junctions and cross-runs beaten clearly upon the earth by the pressure of pads and claws and the drag of tails repeated a hundred times. Men snared rabbits by placing their slip-knots of twisted brass wire, level with a long-eared head, at a place in the run where the animal took its forward bound: so regular were their habits, that they used not only the same paths or runs, but almost the same footmarks.

The tides of the sea were ordered; birds of passage reappeared almost on the same day year after year, swallow to cattle-shed, whitethroat to nettle patch, cuckoo calling in the same dell; salmon left the ocean for their parent rivers; the sharp stars of winter succeeded the pale constellations of summer, and a thousand generations of men were but a moment in their racial history. Thus I had become aware that it was natural to be a creature of habit; and thinking on from that truth, it seemed to me that man was clean and true as a bird or fish or a tree only if he could find freedom from the dead-weight of scholasticism and the chains of an irregular economic system in which lay the fundamental causes of *disorder*.

I should add here that the year was 1926; and like more than one survivor of my generation who lacked historical perspective, I tended to blame the old for what had occurred between 1914–1918, while forgetting that those years gave much that was good in the formation of character: forgetting also, that 'all is experience'.

I noticed, through the jamb of the half-open nursery door, how the child discovered something by chance, and made order from the discovery. Thus one day I saw him picking up his wooden dog and placing it carefully on the window-ledge. After looking at it with pursed mouth for a moment or two, he took it down again, and put it on the rush mat of the floor. Then he put it on the ledge again. It remained there for several minutes, while he was examining his toes; but suddenly he remembered, and scrambled up to get his dog of wood.

The next day he did the same thing with his sponge cake at tea. He took a bite, put it carefully on the plate on the ledge, sat down and crawled away, returned for the cake, sat down and took a bite, put it on the plate and then the ledge again, and went on like that until the cake was finished.

After two visits to the pen, it became my habit to play with the baby for a minute or two about the same time every day. I enjoyed these intervals, and they sobered a little my style of writing. We had a new game—'On the hands—*down*!' He would sit down carefully, turn over and wait on hands and knees until I took his legs by the soft-bone ankle and let him support himself on his hands, as in a wheelbarrow race. A later variation of this game was to shout, from upstairs, 'On the hands—DOWN!' and hearing it, the baby would drop what he was doing and lie on his tummy, while I ran downstairs, my shoes clattering on the treads. One day, peeping down from the window of my little writing-room, I saw him in his pen, now on the lawn with a rug, doing 'On the hands—down!' by himself, one leg waving in the air.

Soon he was crawling up the stairs, over bedroom floor and veranda, through my writing-room, and into the garden. Dangerous stone steps led down, past ferns and 'drunkards'—red and maroon valerian flowers—to the roadway below, where motor cars were beginning to pass now that summer was come. There were also steps, on the northern side, down to the kitchen yard; so I tied one end of a stout string to a strap round his chest and shoulders, the other end to my chair. One moment, as I wrote swiftly, I missed the baby. Where had he gone? Ah, there he was, curled up like a dog on the pony skin, asleep.

Then he was learning to talk like a Devonian. I was writing at my desk when I saw him standing by the garden gate, talking to 'Babe' Carter, aged four, on his way home from school. Hiding my face, I eaves-dropped.

'Ernie, coo!' said 'Babe' Carter. 'Come yurr to look at DaddyWee's li'l ole baby! I zaid "Eh!" and 'a zaid "Eh!" and I zaid "Ah", and 'a zaid "Ah!" and I zaid "Eh!" agen, and 'a zaid "Eh!" agen.'

'Babe' repeated his lesson once more, and each time Windles answered with delight. Not only could he get to the gate and stand upright, but he could talk with other boys like himself!

He was helpful in the house, too. Often he had watched, from his pram, Loetitia cleaning brass; and as soon as he could crawl, he went to the cleaning cupboard, took out rag and tin of Brasso, rubbed the top of the tin, and then the door handle. Once when 'Babe' Carter came home from school, kicking an empty tin, Windles pointed to it, and 'Babe' picked it up and held it out for him. Windles crawled away to the cupboard, got the cloth, and crawling back, gave it to 'Babe'.

He was about thirteen months old when first he showed how easily he could be snubbed. Then his lower lip would go out, and he would turn away, and with knees slightly bent would go to the darkest part of the room or the dampest corner of the garden. Such retreat did not always end in tears, but after a while he came back ready to play again.

'I wonder if he does that for effect, to draw attention to himself?' I said to Loetitia.

'No, I don't think so,' she replied, colouring slightly. I explained that I had done such things as a child; she had obviously not. I wondered how right I was. Conversation about unapparent motives was usually one-sided between us. Was it not natural that the child should want the attention of his mother, even to the exclusion of his father? Loetitia demurred at this idea, as she brought in the baby to say good night.

'Bye-bye, dadda—bye-bye, bath—bye-bye, cold c'eam—bye-bye, Winny.' This last in triumph to the looking-glass.

Sometimes when he was in bed I would run down from the garden-room under its tarred corrugated roof to call Loetitia upstairs to hear music on the headphones of our small valve-with-cat's-whisker Cosmos wireless set—once it was *Peer Gynt*, a marvellous performance with Russell Thorndyke which ended about midnight; or *Tristan und Isolde*—Dvořák's *New World Symphony*—Delius's *Brigg Fair*—and though she came, it seemed to be with reluctance, for it was an interruption in the course of her life. Yet I longed so much to share the feelings I had for Wilfred Owen's poems, and other works from the inner life of the spirit. Such feelings were almost all my life. She would stay and listen; always her thought was how to please me, I knew; but I knew also that our inner worlds did not touch. The baby was all her life.

Often I felt a sense of my own failure when I came upon mother and child, in the little downstairs nursery, hardly more than six feet square, with its cast-iron grate scarcely larger than a scollop shell. What have I done, I said to myself, to interrupt that gentle life, and bring her here to a new environment of ideas, with almost perpetual girding against the present human world. And that poor little boy, can I look after him, that tottering thing with curly hair over his eyes who now carries cake on a plate, cup and saucer, or jug, to the pantry or kitchen, helping his mother, the two of them in this small dark house under a hill, with its down-draught chimneys. And if he models himself on me—there he is copying me by cleaning his teeth, copying me by using brush and comb, copying me by walking with his own stick in the lane—and sometimes trying to shave his four front teeth with my safety razor. He was just three feet high, as measured against the door.

He could not bear to see dirt or mess. If water was spilled, or milk, he was not satisfied until a cloth was fetched and it was wiped up. If he spilled a few drops himself he ran to his mother, saying, 'Ankie, p'ease, Mummy'. All doors must be shut, any tags of paper or string hanging from drawer or cupboard annoyed him. Music delighted; he called it *make*. Always he hurried to hear the wireless, or the gramophone. He had a mouth-organ, sometimes 'playing' himself to sleep with it.

A village maid named Gwennie Brown came to help us in the cottage, and often took the little boy for a walk, while he pushed the go-cart, as it was called, through the flowery lanes, where sometimes a very old woman dressed in early Victorian black clothes and bonnet was to be seen in a sort of dream, as she grazed her son Billy Goldsworthy's cow on the Long Meadow, as the free grass under the hedge was called. I have already given, in *Tales of a Devon Village*, some account of her son's nocturnal living, most of it in the barn adjoining our cottage, as he worked away at his mysterious thumping and bumping by the light of an old lanthorn, until the small hours. Billy Goldsworthy was then nearly sixty; his mother, tall and thin and with a gentle reflective face, with its expression almost entirely detached from the active village life around her, was over eighty. There was a daughter, too, living in the cottage by the stream, who sometimes took her turn at watching Billy's cow as it fed on the herbs and grasses along the lane; and it seemed that she took her turn at wearing her mother's clothes, for when I saw either figure there, I had an impression of almost a twin identity. One day I must write her story, which remains poignantly in memory nearly forty years after I saw the two women standing opposite the village school, in an age which now seems so tranquil and almost static.

Windles loved to see 'Billy Tumpy's Mummie'; the sombre figure smiled at his passing, murmuring less audibly than the whitethroats among the nettles, and more gently. He loved Gwennie, too, and was upset when it was her afternoon off. To pacify him, Loetitia would say, 'Gwennie is going for a nice holiday,' and he was so busy trying to say it that he forgot to cry. 'Nennie ni' 'ordiday!' he came up the garden steps to tell me, with smiling face.

Sometimes when I was singing loudly he cried, ' 'Up, 'up, Dadda!' and was angry if I didn't shut up. Also he would declare, 'Away, Dadda!' if I appeared to be going to interfere with what he was doing.

Gwennie's holiday was every Wednesday afternoon, when the two village shops closed early; and something that happened about ten days after the 'ni' 'ordiday' incident made me wonder if the child realized, from sympathy and not by reason, that it was her relief from duty.

By now he had learned to ask for his pot, by crying out,

'Go, Mumma, go, go!' This during the daytime. His morning relief, despite Loetitia's pre-natal determination to 'train' him from the start—it was a current theory fostered by Dr. Truby King—had been continued in napkins; but now when the snowdrops were appearing in the garden raised above the lane, she had been getting out of bed early to set him on the pot. This he did not like. One frosty morning, as I passed the door of Skullcracker on my way down to get the post which was flung in the open door at 7.15 a.m., I saw Loetitia holding him upright as he squatted, wrapped in a blanket, while she sat in her nightdress—her dressing-gown still on the hook of the bedroom door. She was persuading the child in a low soft voice, and he was protesting with cries and tears. He loathed to feel himself ringed upon the small enamel seat, upon which he was forcibly retained. He was shouting out against inaction, and the phrase he used in protest was 'Ni' 'ordiday! Winny ni' 'ordiday! Ni' 'ordiday! Ni' 'ordiday! Ni' 'ordiday!'

Upturned mats, caught in chairs drawn up to the table; covers of vegetable tureens not sitting flush; a loaf not square on its platter: these sights called forth protests from the child strapped in the high chair, waiting for food to be put on the tray which I myself, thirty years previously, had similarly banged with mug and spoon.

Like the old spaniel which lived with us, the child liked brass band music from the loudspeaker made of stretched calico upon a wooden frame, decorated with coloured blobs of ink shot from various fountain-pens—red, green, black, purple, and brown. The loudspeaker stood on the sideboard in the parlour; and neither dog nor boy could bear reflective music. Dog would howl, boy would yell, 'Up up that rokken noise!' Much later I came across a scrapbook of his maternal grandfather's home and family in mid-Victorian times, and there, playing cricket in the park, was a boy of about six years old with my son's face. Who was it? 'Why, that was Pa when he was a boy!' cried Loetitia, happily. I recalled the old gentleman saying to me, before Windles was born, that the best music ever written was *The Blue Danube Waltz*, and that the music of *Tristan* was a horrible noise. My theory about children, brought up without repression, becoming naturally artistic and musical, and developing the 'highest feelings', etc., got a bit of a shock when one evening the child switched off a Beethoven quartet, before going quietly to the spaniel's 7-lb. tin of small broken pieces of biscuit, to give him his 'num-nums' in peace and quiet.

This was a ritual. Quietly beside the boy, the spaniel would eat a hollow in the biscuit-level, sometimes looking up through floppy ears to give his small friend what looked like a grin. Before the feed the following evening I smoothed level the crater from which the dog had eaten, to mark the level. The child watched this for two evenings in succession; and the third evening, when I brought in the box and set it on the floor, the hollow not smoothed, he ran forward and smoothed it with his hand before allowing 'Biddy' to put his nose in. That was, I said, how all mammals learnt: by imitation. Children were but mammals.

In those days there was beginning a revolution of thought about the education of children; but the ideas were still nascent. I had a chronic fear that if the change in Europe was not hastened, another war would arise, from the same fundamental causes which had made the Great War. This thought was at times almost unbearable; the more so as my novel *The Pathway*, which had been started in the winter of 1924, before my marriage, had been broken off after the New Year, and still lay, only one-fourth done, in my desk upstairs. Three winters had passed, a long time in those days, and still it remained untouched. Too often the repression broke out in rant.

'All the efforts to teach consciously, by reversing the process of imitation, cause the nervous sentinels of a child's mind to resist; and then, if they are subdued, to become dull and inward, and lo! the most valuable period of growth is made negative.'

I tried to explain this to my father-in-law, who had come to pay us a visit.

'Ah,' he replied, as he took up the *Morning Post*, seeking the crossword puzzle.

Some days before, in anticipation of his visit ('The proper place for a dog is the kennel,' he said once), I had bought a tin of flea-powder, and given the spaniel an uneasy half-hour of dusting. My son, finding the empty tin, took off the perforated top, trotted over to the spaniel, and proceeded to shake it over the dog's back. Next he wanted to dust my hair, then his own; after which he fetched his stool to reach grandfather's grey hair.

'Hey, what's this?' exclaimed the old gentleman. 'Ah, good idea! The new education, I see!' before continuing to think out, in eight letters, an object which was round, square, and like the bark of a tree. 'Must be Bill's spaniel,' he muttered.

'Joking apart,' I said, after the laughter, 'your grandson has a fine concern for others. The other morning he was pushing his wooden horse in the lane outside, and when he heard a motor, he pulled Dobbin to the side of the wall and sat on it, after pulling his mother, who had come out of the gate, to the side also. Then he called anxiously to Bill the spaniel, "Motor, Biddy; motor, Biddy; *motor*, Biddy!" As you know, Bill is a bit slow, and knows that motor cars always wait for him to get out of the way. Only when all three of them were safe did Windles smile!'

'Ah yes, we all live and learn,' replied the old gentleman.

Two years later, finding that the village was becoming too popular, while our income was well in excess of the £150 a year on which we had lived without discomfort before the publication of *Tarka* and *The Pathway*, we left for Shallowford, where we were to live for the next seven years, during which time our family increased to four sons and one daughter.

2

On Irritability, Dream, and Death

Here is the valley of the Bray, a clear water stream running over rocks and gravel, past ferns and alders, and haunted by kingfishers, water-ousels, and other wild birds. The cottage was let to us with two miles of trout fishing. Our eldest boy was then three and a half years old, and Baby John was just one year. How it rained during that first winter! The rooms were dark, the thatch always dripping, the wind outside roared in the trees. But at least a new open hearth had replaced the Victorian coal-grate in the sitting-room, and wood from the adjoining deer park was plentiful. Within our fire-place built of old red bricks, beech and oak 'sticks' burned, or smouldered, day and night, giving their warmth to the house. Before leaving the fire, reluctantly, and going to bed, I covered the embers with a layer of ash; and in the morning uncovered them, put a fresh back-stick against the rear bricks and, heaping the embers against its middle, worked from the bellows a gentle stream of air into which soon broke tongues of flame, pale and fretted, from the crimson crackling charcoal. Sometimes while I was working the bellows—the iron spout held afar off, lest the air-stream unduly waste the fire in the embers—the nursery door would open gradually, and turning round, I would observe an eye above a home-made pyjama suit watching me. The door was likely to close again, and then reopen slightly. 'Come in,' I would call, and after hesitation, my elder son would come into the room.

I told him why the bellows must be worked slowly, for a small fire must grow like a tree, and be encouraged gently. Hearing my voice, Baby John would join us, moving rapidly with a sideways flapping movement. He progressed in a succession of smooth jerks, drawing his body along the floor with palms flat on the boards, and his elbows crooked, as a seal uses its flippers when moving up a sandy shore. When the baby was seated beside me, the elder boy was likely to disappear.

By contrast to Windles, 'Bonny' John had an uncomplicated nature. As a baby he lay, patient and tranquil, contemplating with dormouse eyes an inverted world, while on mother's lap his legs were upheld in one hand and the other wound a napkin about his loins. He was nearly asleep before the safety-pin held between her lips was clicked into place. He had to be awakened to take his food; even then, his eyes closed sleepily as soon as he was at the breast; and several times a forefinger had gently to snup his nose to set the little jawbones working again.

Later when he was weaned, and bottle-fed, John often fell asleep with the rubber teat of the bottle resting against his lips. He had a queer way of feeding himself from the bottle. Lying on his back in the pram, he would hold up his legs and clasp the bottle with the soles of his feet. Then, turning it round so that the rubber teat was down towards his mouth, he bent his legs lower until he was sucking. Hands clasping ankles, thus he would sleep for hours when the bottle was empty.

For five months the fire in the new hearth burned continuously, until the ash of tree branches which had fallen in the deer park would have filled half a dozen buckets. After a gale I walked beside the river, noting what torn limbs of ancient trees lay under the Spanish chestnuts, the oaks, the limes, the beeches, and the poplars. For a few shillings, after a word with the Scots forester at the sawmills, enough wood was mine for the following winter. During the summer I sawed and split with wedges the immense boughs, piling them for sun and wind to dry: no irritable, wasteful, sap-hissing fires for me, no black and bodiless embers.

There were five downstair rooms in the cottage, each leading to the other, from the kitchen at the west end to the garden-room at the east. The room next to the garden-room was the day nursery. Here the first-born built tar-engines, steam-rollers, and trains of bricks; and here the second-born knocked them down when they were built. When that happened, Windles would utter a cry of anguish, and retire to some dark corner of the house, where he would grieve alone.

As Baby John grew, I saw how he was like his mother. He was serene, and seemed to be without fear. He was easy about everything. His eyes were wondering and clear. When he learned to talk, the difference in the natures of the brothers was obvious. If Windles was given a box of chocolates, he would say, 'John mustn't have any of these'. Whereas if John were given a box, he would stare with solemn eyes and say, 'Winny must have some'. For all my self-vaunted understanding, I failed to realize the cause of the elder boy's apparent selfishness: he felt himself unwanted, and was as it were fortifying himself with material things. This was my fault, I should have known that he would feel aggrieved, as it were shadowed, since my liking for the new little boy was obvious, because he was immediately approachable, and held out his arms to be picked up; whereas it had seemed, with his brother, that he did not like to be touched, which I suppose I had, in my turn, interpreted that he did not like me, but only his mother.

When I had taken him, a year previously, to see his new brother in a Barnstaple nursing home, Windles had looked at the small sleeping face—pink and with hands resembling claws, while I said, 'Isn't he like a crab? Let's call him Tiny Crab, shall we?'—and he replied, 'Let's crack it up, shall we?'

Now, in our first spring at Shallowford, another baby was on the way. Windles knew about this before his sister was born in April. The new baby had been sleeping during the winter inside Mummy, being made by her.

At that moment in the writing of my book, when I had broken off to go to the river, and had returned, I found a pencilled note on my desk, in Loetitia's handwriting. I had previously asked her to write down anything she might remember of the second boy's infancy. Here are her words. *John was a self-contained baby, never 'naughty', but he was the most mischievous small child I have ever come across. Do you remember your twelve nice new seed-pans?*

Ah yes, those seed-pans!

It was early spring, and we had decided to have a proper garden. At the pottery in Barum we bought twelve clome, or earthenware, seed-pans, twelve inches across, each with a lid. One morning the luminous gossamers of the buoyant air, the blithe singing notes of a chaffinch in the green-gemmed hawthorn hedge, drew me from my writing-room, to plant seeds in the garden. John, who could walk across the lawn almost without having to stop and sit down suddenly, came to watch how seeds were planted. First in the bottom of a pan small pebbles and fragments of rock were placed with shards of a cracked flower-pot, mixed with gravel from beside the river; then some sandy river-silt, with fragments of decaying leaves, also from the river; then a layer of warm damp (but not wet) fibrous well-rotted leaf-mould was spread. This was firmly pressed down, but not too tightly, and seeds were dropped evenly on the top from finger and thumb rubbed together. Naturally (since all young mammals learn by imitation) the two children desired to plant seeds after I had gone indoors to my writing-room, to spend three hours in shadow instead of enjoying myself in the sunshine. Soon Windles went away to play with his toy farmyard, leaving John sitting on the path. There were eleven seed-pans lying in a row beside the garden path when I went in from the garden. Looking out of the window, I saw John lifting one up to bite it. 'Don't break it, Bonny dear,' I called out, and went to my desk. Bill the spaniel was lying on the path asleep in the sun.

When John became properly upright he helped his mother to make the beds, to bake the cakes, to fit together jigsaw puzzles, to turn the sewing-machine handle. He also helped me feed the tame trout in the river, clean the car, saw wood, and paint woodwork. It is true that trout do not feed on stones, that mud is not the best medium for polishing a car radiator, and that wet paint on a lavatory seat can be awkward in the dark; but the will to be helpful was behind all John's efforts. So it was with my new seed-pans. When I came out of the house, having left him alone with them, John pointed proudly to all the work he had done to help with the planting of seeds. Every one of the twelve new clome seed-pans, and the twelve covers which had fitted them so neatly, lay in pieces on the garden path. Some of the pieces had been given to Bi-Bi: there they were, neatly laid out on the flank of the sleeping spaniel.

John was then eighteen months old. He did all sorts of other things in the house to save his parents trouble. In his gentle and unobtrusive way he turned up the lamps to make 'ke'l boiling' (as he called tea), even those lamps designed for illumination rather than for cooking. No warning or explanation by his mother deterred his will-to-be-of-use. So before he turned up a lamp he would look at father or mother, whichever happened to be in the room, and cry out in his high, soft voice, 'Not you look at Bonny now!'

Bonny also helped to do the washing. Once he put five bath towels together with three pairs of pyjamas into the bath which mother had just prepared for the two boys.

Another time he decided to do some ironing in the kitchen. He did not have an iron, but he had a watering-can. Having seen mother sprinkle water on clean clothes before ironing them, he stared at the basket of washing which had just been left by the laundry man who did the washing now that Mum-mum had a baby asleep inside her. Bonny wanted to help Mum-mum, so he filled his watering-can, putting some stones and earth inside because they made the water nicer, and poured it all over the washing piled in the basket.

One morning Loetitia and I set out in the car, meaning to go to our old village, and, leaving the car in the sunken lane, to walk round the headland which lay out into the far, blue-sky-dreaming Atlantic. It was a thought almost unbearable at this period of my life that the April month should pass without myself walking through the wind-sheered trees of North Side, and along the sheep-paths through the bracken and ling, and onwards into the open vastness of ocean and air, where above high cliffs the gulls wheeled and cried, and the ravens of the Point twirled and deeply croaked, with perhaps the thrilling sight of a peregrine falcon drawing a steep black line down the sky.

It was a clear sunny day, and we stopped in Barum to buy some pasties and apples. When she came out of the pastrycook's shop Loetitia looked strange, and in answer to my question said she had a slight pain, but it was nothing, she thought she had indigestion. It was then about noon. I said I would take her to the nursing home at once, but she replied it was nothing really, perhaps it was the stewed rhubarb she had eaten for supper the night before. But I took her to the nursing home, and then went to look at the books in the Athenaeum, and stare out of the window at the river and the passing life on the Long Bridge. After gazing at the exhibits of rock and fossil in the museum downstairs, and staring at the lovely back and shoulder line of the plaster cast of the Greek girl in the hall, I went outside again and had a pint of beer at Mr. Dening's tavern in the High Street. From there I rang up the nursing home, and the Matron's voice said, 'Oh, is that you, Mr. Williamson? We've been hoping to get in touch with you. Half an hour after you left, a fine baby girl was born. Yes, Mrs. Williamson is well and happy. Won't you come round? You'll be in time to have lunch with her.'

I went into the bar, shook the astonished Mr. Dening by the hand—as a young man he had known Loetitia's grandfather, who had fought as an ensign at Balaclava—and feeling free as the house-martins flying up and down the High Street, went round to see my daughter.

She had dark eyes, and much dark hair, like a Japanese doll, on her head. Loetitia, rosy and laughing and happy, was sitting up against a heap of pillows. She said: 'What a shame, we've spoiled your walk for you—the naughty little thing was three days early!'

Baby Margaret lay naked in the pram, in the shade of the yew tree growing out of the lawn, while Windles and John played in the deer park seen through the iron gates across the lane. Sometimes she lay on her back, staring with large dark eyes at the sky, at rooks flying over, and swallows, while apple-blossom drifted upon her nakedness, as she slept like an inverted frog, all Danaë to the drift of pollen from the limes just inside, where laboured innumerable bees to fill the pollen-bags upon their thighs. And then summer was gone once more, and she was crawling about the house, to be seen, suddenly, in odd corners, her dark hair wild over her face, and two almost sombre eyes staring out of shadow.

Another day during the winter some friends came to tea and stayed to supper, and afterwards we sat before the wood fire and listened to *Tristan and Isolde* on the gramophone. The sitting-room was lit by two candles and the flames of the oakwood fire. There were ten of us, sitting in a semicircle in the small room. On the left of the circle were the two horse-hide armchairs, then an old sofa, then a wicker chair, beside it a small leather chair used by Loetitia and brought in from the nursery, then a wheel-back yew-wood chair, then a ten-year-old milking-stool which I had, in a burst of enthusiasm, bought for a guinea from a Bideford antique dealer before the crash of 1929. It so happened that the half-circle around the fire was arranged with chairs that diminished in size from one end to the other. During a pause in the music—divine irradiance of human longing on the very borders of death—when every one was quiet and still, the nursery door handle was turned, and again turned, before the door was pushed slightly open, and there came the creak of a wicker-work chair being pushed through the space. It was a very small chair, about twelve inches high only, and it belonged to John, who came gently after it, carrying it in his arms and placing it carefully at the end of the semicircle before sitting down on it and holding out his hands to the warmth of the fire. He did it serenely, quietly, entirely without shyness or self-consciousness. The child warmed his hands for a few moments, staring at the flames; then he said, turning to me, 'More bungycar'. The gramophone was bungycar.

He sat there, listening to the music, unspeaking, until he felt tired, when he got up, lifted his chair in his arms, and went through the door again, closing it behind him. Later we found him asleep in Baby Margaret's pram, into which he had climbed.

One morning I saw the little boy sitting alone in his wicker chair, his eyes dull, his head drooping to one side.

There was a pink spot on each cheek. His head felt hot. He spoke almost in a whisper. Yes, Bonny wanted 'vor go bade' (bed). So I put him to rest in my big horse-hide chair. He lay still, just as I set him there. Loetitia carried him to his cot upstairs. Next day he had a temperature of nearly 105 degrees. It was broncho-pneumonia. He got worse. Loetitia nursed him in her arms at night. It developed to pulmonary pneumonia, and also pleurisy, with congestion in one lung. He demanded to be taken out of his cot, and put in my chair.

'No no no no, Dad-dad's chair, not Bonny's bade, damn Bonny's bade!' protesting in a weak wail at any attempts to tuck him up in the cot. When Loetitia told me this I carried him downstairs, and put him in my chair, and at night the other horse-hide chair was set against it, to form a bed for Loetitia. As the days and nights drew on and the child grew paler and thinner, he protested against almost everything, even his mother's presence. He would not drink from any cup held by her. 'Ke'l boilin',' he would cry, struggling to sit up. *Ke'l boilin'* was his word for tea, by which he meant a drink of water. 'No no no no,' pushing away his own cup.

Next he demanded Windles's cup. So the water was poured into Windles's cup; but this caused a wail of protest. 'No no no no, Daddy cup ke'l boilin' '—and this too was pushed away by the little claw-like hand, while from his drooping lips issued an impotent grizzling noise which tore at my very life.

After a week, during which period he was nursed by an almost unsleeping mother, he was so weak that he could not struggle to a sitting position without a supporting hand behind the sharp shoulder-blades and another hand behind the thin neck and the rolling, wobbling head.

'Winny cup ke'l boilin', no no no, Daddy cup, no no no damn Mummy cup ke'l boilin', Bonny cup ke'l boilin',' hour after hour, Loetitia with dark rings under her eyes and myself standing helplessly by. He drank, wheezing and choking, only if my hand supported him.

The doctor paid his eighth visit. 'Keep him warm,' he said. 'He will be all right.'

When the doctor came again he stared at the near-skeleton. At last he repeated, 'Keep him warm. He'll be all right soon,' and after staring again, in the attitude of one sharing the parents' feelings, departed.

The neck white and stalk-like: chin sharp and frail: wasted body almost transparent.

Nine days now like that; seven nights for Loetitia without sleep, the dry husky irritable wail growing thinner and weaker.

On the ninth evening Loetitia came to me, with a red, hurt face. She leaned her head on my shoulder, crying. She had cried only twice before in her life, on the death of her mother when she was a schoolgirl of seventeen, and again, after the slightest of misunderstandings, when we were first engaged to be married.

'He pushed me away, he is crying for you. Then he had a sort of convulsion, and now he lies so still—' her whispered words broke. It had come.

I felt a chill pass into me; the hair of the back of my head felt to be raised. Putting her in my chair before the fire, and telling her I would not permit the child to die, I went downstairs, feeling an extraordinary strength and resolution come upon me. It was like a dream.

In the sitting-room, wrapped in blankets on the large

chair, the child was lying, its head on one side. Kneeling down, I saw a pus of yellow matter about the exposed ear, and also the eyelids were set with a crust of the same matter. I took the child's dry hands in my hands, holding them firmly, and began to will the thread of life in him to be not broken.

Kneeling by the chair, holding the hands and wrists, I felt myself drawing together, almost to a solidity of non-feeling, which forced itself upon the child. For about a minute the assembled and directed solidity of myself did not move; then I felt a flow through my wrists, and from my head. It was as though the struggle of the life-thread was now within myself, my eyes were streaming, and my head began to ache. It was a relief, for something told me our lives were now joined, and I knew my intuition was true. The child seemed to be sleeping.

That night I slept in the chair opposite him, before the glowing oak logs on the piled ash of the hearth. Had I been selfish before, leaving him all night with his mother? Now she was sleeping, for the child's life had passed to me. In the morning the fever's rage in him was less, and we knew he would live. I did not like to think to myself that I had done anything to save his life. It was an instinctive act, I was not responsible. Soldiers coming out of battle could not talk about what they had felt, truly; their minds avoided the exposure. Otherwise many would have lost their reason. They made light of their personal feelings, let them be covered by the mass consciousness. But when they saw printed accounts in the paper of their cheeriness after battle, they were blasphemous.

It was Loetitia, by her unceasing care and fortitude during the nine days and nights, sleeping only in uneasy, broken snatches, who had nursed the child and sustained the strength of his body against disintegration and death. It was only at the crisis, briefly, that the father's will or spirit was of any use.

When the doctor came next he said, 'I thought that we were going to lose him'.

3

Cold Pudding is the Family Friend

There were tame Loch Leven trout in the pool below the deer park bridge. I bought them during our first spring at Shallowford, and fed them regularly in spring and summer. Visitors were taken to the bridge, a hundred paces from the cottage, and as soon as a handful of dried fish-food was scattered below, the water was rocking and a-flip with heads and spotted flanks and slashing tails. Almost every day in spring and summer I stood on the bridge, watching the fish. Occasionally I said to Windles, 'Coming to feed the fish?' as I left the house about noon, and always received the prompt reply, 'No thanks'. He spoke as though he were thwarting a desire to come. Once he said, 'Bonny is nicer to take than me, I know,' and turned away.

Noon was the best time to see the fish in the higher pool above the bridge. The sun shone directly down into the clear water, lighting every red and black spot of the familiar trout, every caddis-house on the stones and the coloured fragments of gravel. It was pure, beautiful water, flowing down the valley from the rock and the peat-bed of Exmoor. John was always willing to 'sheed-er-shish'. Hand in hand we went with the toffee tin and the nickel spoon to the garage, where in a tub the dry food was kept. I used to bend low as I walked up the steep hump of the bridge, lest my shadow be thrown across the water and the fish shoot away to the dark alder roots under the bank. John was much smaller than the parapet, and I had placed a special footstone at the lowest place for him to stand on. It was amusing to watch him walking by himself to 'sheed-er-shish', and when he got to the bridge, carefully bending double, although his shadow fell far short of the top of the stone parapet.

There were long blank periods in the valley, when no writing was done, and life seemed to be standing still, even to have passed one by. Heavens, how fast Time was flowing away with life. And it had really hardly begun! Yet here was Windles, walking about by himself under the lime trees, strangely excited, because he was wearing a new satchel. Starting school on Monday!

Yesterday it seemed to be winter, and spring would never come: today it is midsummer, and the bees humming loudly in the lime trees just inside the park gates, the blossoms broken out of the sheaths. Another springtime lost to life, scarcely seen, and my little boy already growing up! Windles wearing his new dinner-bag, and feeling so important, and also a little fearful, for the new world of school which he was to enter on Monday morning. Windles going to school, Windles five years old! O world, O life, O Time, I cried with the ghost of Shelley; and then the west wind was streaming away the leaves of the trees, the river was high and grey as the sky, the fall run of salmon was over, and winter come again.

It was cold in that valley during winter. Mists formed over the water. They hung on the frosted air, in still layers a few feet above the grass and the rush-clumps. It was a commonplace thing now, Windles walking to school—no longer an adventure—two miles across the park, round by the gardens and terraces of 'the big house', across a field to the village school. Two miles in the frosty early morning, two miles back again at night. On Saturdays he had a holiday.

'Coming for a walk, Windles?'

'No, thanks.'

Loetitia was always busy, washing, ironing, cooking, mending, happily talking with Windles, John and Baby Margaret. In December the salmon spawned, when the dead leaves had ceased turning over in the grey water swilling by the alder roots and roaring over the falls. In February came the frosts, following on weeks of little rain. The river was low, and many copper-coloured, thin salmon with fungus-yellow patches on jaw, tail, and flank were seen in the shrunken pools. Sometimes I found them lying at the edge of the shallow water, too dazed or exhausted to move away. After months of endurance, without feeding, in fresh water, they had spawned; and having fulfilled themselves, were relict of life. Otters travelled up and down the river, catching many of the kelts, as they were called, and leaving them, with torn shoulders, in the shallows. Foxes and crows pulled and picked the carcasses, revealing the spiky backbones; rats came afterwards, their footprints and dragging tails clearly shown on the sandy scours. I put many fish, which were lying half-dead in the shallows, into the pools, where they moved slowly away into darkness: until delirium set them roving again, and coming to the swifter water at the tail of the pools, they were carried down and left helpless on the stickles. It was sad to see them, these noble fish which had been so strong and keen in their sea-strength, porcelain-white and silver-blue, now despoiled and enfeebled by the very impulse which gave them life.

There the kelts lay, in the still, ice-ringed pools of the river on whose banks I walked, always alone. 'Care to come for a walk, Winny, and see the salmon?'

'No, thanks.' Always the same quick reply.

One night Loetitia said, with an obvious effort, 'Windles is afraid of you.'

'Of *me*?'

'He thinks you don't like him.'

'But he doesn't seem to like me!'

'He thinks you like John better.' She added, smiling and flushed with nervousness, 'John *is* very companionable, isn't he?'

I stared at the nursery fire. We were having supper together there, for once.

'Don't be hurt,' said Loetitia. 'But you make Windles afraid, I think. Sometimes those things you say to him, he says afterwards, "Are there *really* green eyes in the wood?" to me. He is very nervous, you know, and also has a dread of making a fool of himself before you. And don't mind my saying this, but he is really *terrified* of "green eyes". After all, he *is* only six, and has a vivid imagination.'

Windles came into the room, in pyjamas, slippers, and his cousin's cast-off dressing-gown. He had come to his mother for what, at four years, he had called his 'little readities'. The boy was waiting for me to go, so that he could draw his wicker-chair to the fire, and sitting by his mother's knee, be enchanted by the story she would read to him. She had read to him, many times, *A Little Boy Lost*, *The Story of a Red Deer*, *Black Beauty*, and *The Cock, the Mouse, and the Little Red Hen*.

They waited for me to go, but I said: 'I'm going into the deer park tomorrow, in hopes of seeing the dear little man again. He is so friendly, and has a very snug home in that old oak tree. I hope he won't put the magic on me! Fancy, he's only about half the size of Windles!'

Windles's eyes were round. Then he looked puzzled. 'Who is, Dad?'

'He loves cold Christmas pudding best,' I said to Loetitia. 'I put a slice at the foot of the tree this morning, and pretended not to look, but I saw him coming down, he grabbed it, and was up the trunk again quickly. He has such tiny little hands, much smaller than Baby Margaret's. I hope no one shoots him, it will be such a shame.'

Windles looked alarmed.

'I don't know what his real name is, but as elves like to be called queer names, I should think if we were to call out "Cold Pudding!" he would come. Not rudely, or cheekily, or he might put the magic on me. In fact, it's best always to praise him. Say "My Lord", rather deferentially, for he is a bit vain, and likes to pretend he's a lord.'

'What does vain mean, Mum?' inquired Windles quickly.

'Oh, a bit stuck-up,' murmured Loetitia.

'Is Cold Pudding *really* true, Dad?' he asked earnestly.

'Well, I'll tell you what, you come with me tomorrow, and I'll show you the oak tree, and we'll stand under it and say the magic rhyme

Cold Pudd!
Cold Pudd!
Come down if you would!

and we *may* see him. He likes being praised, especially for his horsemanship. But of course'—I whispered, looking round, and over my shoulder—'really he rides an old ewe, and pretends it's a hunter, like one of those out to grass in the deer park. Once he got on a ram, and you should have seen how it flung him off! He went head over heels into the river! But I didn't laugh, of course. I just said, "Ah, my Lord, how I admire such patience in schooling that wild Tartar stallion! And what a splendid diver you are, you went right in with scarcely a splash! Your Lordship will relish a slice of cold pudding after such strenuous exercise, I'll warrant. Permit me to leave it just by this root." Of course I didn't look at him direct, as elves hate being stared at. But I know he heard, because when I did look round, the slice of pudding was gone, and I found a little basket of mushrooms at the foot of the tree. He's a very kind little elf, and does no harm to any one. I'll be seeing him tomorrow morning, I hope.'

Windles was looking from his mother's face to my face with a new look in his eyes. 'Please, may I come? Or perhaps you'd prefer John,' he added.

'I think I'll take you first, Windles. John is so very small, isn't he. Later, perhaps, you can take him and show him where Cold Pudding lives. I know that with you, his big brother, John will be safe. Tomorrow we'll go, just you and I, shall we?'

'Yes, please!' cried Windles. His eyes were shining.

I left the room at once, a little ashamed of this uneasy substitute for—what?

It was not until long afterwards that one realized that the theory, generally accepted in the 'twenties, of bringing up small children without a fuss of affection, without cuddling, was wrong. We must regard them not as pets, lest a lavishment of emotion in later life give them complexes—the fashionable word of the anti-Victorian twenties. This was as unnatural a theory as that of spare-the-rod-and-spoil-the-child which it had replaced.

So the eldest child had had no animal warmth from his male parent during his earliest years; while John, by his more complacent nature and odd independent ways, had drawn forth tenderness.

Or was it deeper than that, a difference of genetic traits which set human beings apart before consciousness develops? Or, more simply, the first-born feeling unwanted when the second child arrives, because the father lacks awareness of the inner feelings of the displaced child?

During the summer that followed, Cold Pudding became an interesting local character for Windles and John. Sometimes he came into the house, first turning the magic on himself and becoming invisible, of course; at other times we saw him in the woods, in the guise of a squirrel, or an owl, and once we all heard the splash of his dive into the salmon pool below the railway viaduct. I said it might be a salmon, now that it was autumn, and the big fish were moving up river to spawn, but no, Windles was sure he had seen Cold Pudding's little black button-boots.

It was again summer, and children playing in the grass, or naked by the glittering river over which the kingfisher sped like a sapphire fleeing from the fate of imprisonment in a precious stone. Sometimes we bathed together, I in the deep pool below the bridge while the children splashed and shouted in the fast broken water below the dam of stones we had heaved and set across the river to raise the level of the trout pool. Windles and John were now friends, but not exactly John and Baby Margaret!

A familiar sight: Margaret sitting on the floor with two handfuls of John's fair hair, the black stumps of her baby-teeth bared; John holding her dark hair in his hands, pulling as hard as she was pulling. To any witness, both would complain together:

'Bonny } is pulling my hair!'
Margy }

Were Baby Margaret's teeth bad because Loetitia's food and drink at Shallowford had not provided calcium for their making? As she grew to walking age, so her teeth rotted one by one, and when she smiled, top and bottom rows were seen to be black stumps. As a baby she had tried to eat earth in the deer park, a habit always restrained by her nanny; but earth Margaret ate again when no one was there to startle her big brown eyes with, 'No no, baby, aa-ah, dirty girl, Margy!'

Margy used to crunch up egg-shells and swallow them. As soon as I heard of this habit I realized that it was the baby's instinctive search for calcium, which built bones! So I bought some vitamin D halibut oil globules, and saw that she swallowed them.

It seemed no time before Baby Margaret was following her brothers to that fascinating place, the railway station, a mile away up the hill beyond the iron railings of the deer park. John and she would sometimes go away in the early morning, and be seen again only at night.

Once in answer to my question, Loetitia said, 'Oh, they're all right, I expect. They go in various cottages, and get food.'

'But aren't you worried that something might happen to them? Margy isn't two yet, is she?'

'She was three last month! They know how to look after themselves.' I thought this sang-froid admirable, a counter to my often fussy anxiety, but one day I had a shock.

There was a viaduct spanning the valley, with a single track to carry the trains from Paddington to the Atlantic coast and back. Stone pillars rose high above the river, the haunt of jackdaws which nested under the sleepers. Seen from Humpy Bridge, where we fed the trout, toy trains puffed across, drawing trucks which in silhouette looked like pictures of those pulled by Stephenson's Rocket. One Sunday morning, as I was walking up river, I saw a small figure moving across the viaduct, a framework of iron black against the blue sky. As I watched, there appeared behind it a smaller figure; and far behind, a scarcely perceptible tot.

The sight was alarming. I had often crossed the viaduct myself, to look down two hundred feet upon grass, trees, and curiously flat river below; and occasionally to launch paper gliders. I knew well the dangers; for once, as I had been cutting a paper sail-plane with scissors, the sudden swelling roar of a train increasing loudly told me that one had just come through the tunnel. Pressing myself against the open iron criss-cross parapet, holding decayed woodwork, I felt the space between my body and the near rail was not enough for the train to pass without striking my body. The self-magnifying engine-front thundered upon me, and it seemed that my coat-tails would be torn by one or another of the carriages. However, I had survived —and now, up there my three children, spaced one far behind the other along the thousand feet of aerial railroad, were slowly walking! I watched them to invisibility among the spruce trees, and met them later in the deer park, to which they had descended through the plantation of Japanese larches growing on the hillside. They promised they would never go there again, for, I said, Cold Pudding had been terribly upset, as well as myself. I thought it better to make a picture in their minds, rather than reveal parental anxiety through exhortation.

As has been described, Windles was the first to hear of the elf who lived in the oak tree. He had gone there with me, holding my hand. Under the tree he had repeated, rather quickly and nervously:

Cold Pudd!
Cold Pudd!
Come down if you would!

Cold Pudding wouldn't; and after a while Windles had said, 'Is it *true*, Dad?'

'How can I say, Windles? Is the oak tree true? Who makes it put out its leaves every spring?' Then whispering, 'And look, that small round hole up there! A woodpecker hacked that out with its beak, and then made a bottle-shaped room inside, for its nest. But the branch was hollow, the eggs would have fallen through the cracks of the rotten wood, and so the bird went away, leaving a fine spy-hole for Cold Pudding. Look, Windles! Do you see a bright little brown eye behind the hole? It's gone now. Oh dear, I hope he isn't angry. Let's speak loudly in his favour.' Then aloud: 'His Lordship has lived here many years, in this forest monarch. He is a superb horseman, and an even better diver into the river.' I flickered my left eyelid at Windles. 'And how he can fly! The other day I had the great pleasure of observing his Lordship in his airplane. It was magnificent flying!' In a whisper, 'Actually he got two white paper bags from somewhere, tied them to his arm, and jumped off the highest branch up there, and though he flapped his arms frenziedly, all he did was to come straight, but slowly, to the ground, for the bags filled themselves with air and acted as parachutes. He squeaked with fear, and tried to put the magic on himself, to make himself invisible, but he couldn't do that, as his feet were not on the earth. Ah yes, my boy, his Lordship is a very fine all-round athlete—h'm yes, especially all round the sheep—I beg pardon—the hunters —he rides, indeed his favourite position seems to be hanging round their necks——'

'Ha, ha!' laughed Windles.

'Sssh! He may be listening! I wonder if he is? You watch up there. If displeased a shower of earth is liable to fall upon us at any moment.'

Windles stared at the hole; and the next moment, just after Father had knelt beside him, staring with him, a loose shower of earth fell upon Windles. He looked startled.

'I thought so! I've vexed him by what I said. What shall we do?'

Windles thought. 'I wonder if there's any cold pudding at home?'

We went home to find out. There was sultana pudding. The very thing! We put it at the front of the tree, then turned our backs and walked away. When we went back, the pudding was gone. A jackdaw flew around.

'I believe he had it,' said Windles.

'Possibly. Cold Pudding may have sent him. After all, Cold Pudd is a lord, you know. Besides, all the birds and animals are his devoted subjects. Cold Pudd knows them all.'

And so, after the railway viaduct incident, I used the elf to impress their minds.

'Yes, children, Cold Pudding is a very tender-hearted

person, and knows well the dangers of walking on the viaduct, especially today.'

Windles looked puzzled. Then he said, 'But, Daddy, didn't Cold Pudding know that there were no trains on Sunday?' Then with a smile, and uplifted eyebrows, 'I understand, Father, we won't go there again.' And loyally kept the secret.

4

On Terriers, Ghosts, Trout, and Sport

John liked gardening. All the children had a garden, but only John took a crop off his square yard of ground beside the compost pit. The crop was seven peapods. He had planted lettuces, radishes, beans, peas, and conkers but only a few straggling pea-plants had managed to grow. A lot of worms and slugs lived in the compost heap. So John stuck up a notice on a piece of paper:

PRIVATE
For slugs to keep away

John was going to school now, carrying Windles's old dinner-bag, while Windles had a new, larger one. Once as Loetitia and I, dressed in our best clothes, were setting off for a cocktail party in Barum, we met a queer little long-haired boy, his stockings down over his shoes, and the pockets of his shapeless reach-me-down jacket bulging with granite chips picked off a dump beside the London road. He was walking home alone. He had a thin, delicate face with luminous eyes, almost hidden by a thatch of long fair hair. Was this the little thing that had so nearly died? Another time, Windles's pockets were weighed down with pieces of rusty old iron given away by the blacksmith. The boys were 'collecting for a museum'.

Margaret was quick and vivid; a dark, warm child. John and she seemed ever to be laughing, playing, and fighting together. At one time they had a habit of locking themselves in the lavatory, behind the green baize door on the stairs, whence shrieks of laughter would come. I did not bother about what they were doing, they were young puppies at play. An unrestricted life in childhood was right for them. Sometimes they swore, using words which everyone knows, or should know. Windles had passed out of the period of intensive swearing; indeed, sometimes he checked me with a slight frown, 'Dad!' merging into a smile. I liked this, wanting him not to feel inferior to me.

About this time we got a dog, to replace the old spaniel which had died. It was a fox-terrier which we had bought from the children's nurse, who was locally known as Galloping Annie, because during the war she used to whip-in to a pack of foxhounds on the moor. Galloping Annie had kept house and home for Arthur Heinemann, a Bohemian sportsman who had recently died. As has been told in the companion book to this, *A Clear Water Stream*, Arthur had been a master of otterhounds, keeping tamed otters and badgers; he had known as much about the wild life of the moor as anyone. I wished I had seen him more frequently during his life: the usual human regret: we do not realize what is lost until it is too late.

After his death, Galloping Annie came to Shallowford,

bringing one or two of Arthur's famous breed of terrier with her. Margy was then sleeping in the cot. Every night, when I went to say good night to her, she told me she had seen the 'ghose'—a ghost. I wondered if she meant Cold Pudding, and asked her.

'No, 'tes the ghose, 'tidden no Cold Pudden, 'tes the ghose,' she whispered, sitting up in bed, her brown hair as usual almost hiding enormous dark eyes. We never knew if she were terrified or not. I decided that the idea of a ghost probably came from Windles, and the prints he began to absorb at an early age—weekly papers with such names as *The Big Shot*, and *The Champion*. The fictional feasts in them were Lucullan compared with my homely slices of cold pudding.

For days and weeks Margy used to greet one of us with the whispered words, 'The ghose!'

The ghose turned out to be a large mouse which visited her every evening for the fragments of biscuits she left scattered on the counterpane of her cot. One night Loetitia saw it sitting on her pillow, nibbling a bit in its paws, while Margy, also sitting on the pillow, regarded it with owl-eyes. 'The ghose!' she whispered, as it scurried off the pillow, and rattled over the polished beech-wood floor, and into its hole in the wainscoting. Margy said she loved her ghose. When the mouse began to bring its children, Loetitia had to bribe them to keep away from the cot by placing saucers of milk and biscuits under the cot. I did not know of this until one evening I went in, and a drove of the little creatures scampered away for their hole. The same female mouse had gathered wool from Margy's blankets for its nest, Loetitia told me. This reminded me that John when a baby used to pull feathers out of his eiderdown, for birds flying in the open window to pick up for their nests. Margy's ghose used to drag large pieces of biscuit across the floor, with loud noises, to the hole in the corner.

Returning after the Whitsun holidays, I saw the children gathered round Galloping Annie, who was sitting on a chair in the kitchen and holding on her lap a young badger.

'Look what Annie's got for you, Dad,' said Margaret, as my heart sank, for yet another responsibility.

The small grey animal was wild, frightened, lying very still. Galloping Annie was what I never was, a real sporting character. In her spare time she bred Parson Jack Russell terriers; it was an ordinary thing for her, when she heard of a calf dying, or possibly born dead, to get hold of it, cut it up, and boil portions of it in a crock, to feed to the dogs. While kindly looking after the children, she retained the mastership of a badger digging club; but no longer was she one of the whippers-in to a moorland pack of foxhounds. Her great friend, Arthur Heinemann, had defended me against a charge of writing unnatural history in *Tarka* made by Miss Frances Pitt in a review of the book in one of the weeklies. It was about the skinning of frogs by otters, before they ate them. Miss Pitt had declared that her tame otters gobbled frogs, skins and all; Arthur declared that he had seen 'frogs skinned back to the eyes' left by wild otters on river banks.

Later, he told me privately that he considered I had 'the taint', or humanitarian feelings which, when applied to descriptions of hunting, etc., would mar those descriptions, by bringing in bias. A potential writer in the class of Nimrod would be spoiled if he allowed private feelings to 'taint' objectivity. Of course he was right; but then

I was not and never had been a purely sporting writer, I once said. 'More's the pity,' Arthur replied, as we drank his potent cider in the cottage near Wiveliscombe.

Now, looking at the small badger, I said, 'Aren't they rather hard to tame?' while thinking of that double-lock bite, which had cracked more than one terrier's lower jaw.

'I'll tame it soon,' said Galloping Annie. 'Arthur and I tamed foxes, otters, badgers—oh, easy.'

Every afternoon she took it from the shed in the garden (my carpentry room, seldom visited at that time) and stroked it on her lap while sitting in the kitchen, while the tottering Robert stood by her knee and watched her. The animal never moved on her lap. It crouched, while the hand (now gloved, I noticed) soothingly stroked its pate.

'I'll tame it. Dear little thing.' And in a tender voice, 'Frightened by the terrier when we dug it out, that's what makes it afraid, see? I'll tame it, see if I don't. I've tamed many. Arthur had one which followed him everywhere. Brockie we called it.'

'Yes, I remember Arthur telling me about it, Annie.'

'That farmer, near Minehead it was, who caught it in one of his gins, wanted it killed, as it was after his chickens. Arthur went down to the field with him. Brockie stood up and whimpered, the gin on its hind leg, and tried to touch Arthur's hand with its paw. The farmer saw it crying like a child, and said he wasn't going to ask Arthur to kill such a little beauty. You'll see, I'll tame this cub all right.'

But the young badger remained wild, and one night Annie let it go. It went up through the dark fir-plantations behind the house, where there was good cover, and plenty of rabbits. There were also, but in the winter only, plenty of rabbit gins.

We also had a succession of cats about the place, but always the cat of the moment used to go after rabbits, and get caught in one of the snares set in Bremridge Wood.

I bought the fox-terrier from Galloping Annie because it looked so small and clean and alert, a puppy not more than eight inches long when first I saw it walking up the garden path. It grew up very spirited, entirely without fear. One day the smallholder from whom we had our milk came to me and said he had lost some pullets, but had found three of them, partly de-feathered, in the hedge. He added that he had an idea my terrier was responsible.

'Really,' I said, 'you astonish me! That little dog!' and reminded him of the numerous foxes which lived in Bremridge Wood.

'Ah yes,' he said laughing, 'we know all about the foxes, too.'

'Well,' I replied, 'I knew there were chickens about, for every year I have found it almost impossible to retain any seeds in my vegetable garden, so industriously are they scratched up almost as soon as sown.'

'Yes,' he said, 'we too find that'; but hadn't I noticed the great number of pheasants in my garden every morning? He or his wife or small son, bringing the morning milk, invariably set any number from half a dozen to a score running for the hedge. I promised to keep an eye on the dog, though with being fully occupied with writing all day at the moment, and half the night, my eyes were not of much use, I said.

'One can't have it both ways, farmer: natural reality or vitality in books is only achieved by the loss of personal life.'

'Ah, that's what it is, is it? I often wonder why you look so worried.'

'You hear me shouting and yelling, I know, farmer; believe me, writing is a most unnatural thing, and the better the books, the more a man loses thereby from his life. But the trouble is not writing, but *not writing*. "He who desires, but acts not, breeds pestilence," as William Blake said.'

The farmer looked at me with less respect than before, so I changed the line. 'I'm taking up carpentry now, and am making a three-legged table, so I will go and work in the stable, where I've a bench; natural work is hand-work! One day I'll chuck all this unnatural business of imagining things and putting them on paper, day after day, month after month, year after year—or rather, as I said, *not* putting them on paper—if you get my meaning—and be like you, a farmer, a natural man. Meanwhile, are you sure it isn't rats who have mauled your pullets?'

'Well, it may be, sir, but I've seen your li'l old white dog about my place recently.' He laughed again; and whistling, I went away to try and finish the rickety, creaking table I was making for Loetitia.

The first thing I saw was my terrier, who dashed away from a heap of shavings under the bench. And among the shavings were three more pullets with feathers torn from their breasts, as by the worrying of teeth.

When all the missing pullets were paid for, I was advised to tie one of them round the terrier's neck, to humiliate him. But a big dog came round the corner, there was a short sharp fight, and the big dog ate the chicken.

More pullets were killed, and I had to beat the terrier. He tried to bite me while I was beating him, and I respected him for it. Why should any dog be beaten, indeed? Why had I bought the little brute, hadn't I enough worries already?

The next day the terrier fought a young cockerel and killed it, then he slew half a dozen hens. I learned this during tea. I'd been writing ten hours a day for the past fortnight, beautiful summer weather lost, and could eat nothing.

During tea John and Margy began to giggle. Windles muttered, 'Shut up, our father's worried.' John giggled the more.

'Go on,' I said, 'have a burst of laughter, get it out of you.' I remembered how I had loved, and dreaded, a giggle when I was young, and my father was worried, and how mother had irritated him by trying to hush the children, herself being always a little fearful of, or rather dreading, my father's irritability. John and Margy began to giggle again. 'Go out to the kitchen!' I yelled, and they hurried out, gasping with laughter.

After a while Margy opened the door leading from the kitchen, and tried to say something. 'Go away!' I shouted, and the door was closed instantly. Loetitia looked tired, the coming baby was a strain to her. The thought of that was worrying. Also the book being written was, I dreaded, all wrong, it would have to be rewritten, though that would only mean a variation of detail, not of theme or temper; the temper was wrong. A publisher had read a third of it, had advised its abandonment. I could not believe him, I was a fool to expose a part-formed embryo to the light, to alien eyes. Besides, hadn't various people told me the same sort of thing about every book I had written? Hadn't one publisher even advised me that the 'cosmic references' in *Tarka* didn't come off, and spoiled what the trade otherwise might possibly take up as a good animal story for children? There were enough doubts in a writer's mind, without adding to them the doubts of a publisher or a publisher's reader. Always these doubts must be beaten down, and kept down, while a book was being written.

Loetitia sat opposite me, absorbed by her own thoughts, yet worried because I was worried. The baby she was making, and the constant work, and the worry about me, made her look weary at times. The physical embryo within her was alive; the poetic or psychical embryo within me was mortified. We had no point of contact. The poetic embryo was solely a man's affair, there could be no sharing of it. It was unnatural, decadent, the intensive burning away of life in imagination.

'Damn those children,' muttered Windles, as shouts and shrieks came from the kitchen. The front-door knocker thumped, I got up and saw the farmer standing there. He held a bedraggled Rhode Island cock by the legs. It was an old cock, and one that had terrified Margaret, by running at her. It had driven strange cats away, and was a very fierce old bird, with big spurs. Or had been—until the terrier had killed it.

When the farmer had gone, I shut the terrier in the nursery, and ran down to the swamp to cut a withy from one of the willows growing there. Then to finish my tea. The noise from the kitchen was intensive. I went in, and saw an amazing sight. The two children, with flushed faces, had apparently been sliding on the floor, on a mixture of cream and something else. The cream bowl was in pieces on the floor. John had the garden besom in his hands, and was pushing the mess about the oilcloth. The sight enraged me and taking off my leather braces, and pulling Margy by the arm, I cut her thrice, but not hard, across the bare legs. Then I went for John, who cried out, 'Don't you hit me, you bloody old fool, you!' I pulled him by the arm, into the dining-room, and each time the leather braces swished he sat down on the floor. He yelled with anger and fright, for never before had he been treated like this. I cut him across the legs and tears came in his eyes.

Meanwhile Windles was in great agitation, clenching his fists and waving his arms, his face agonized, as he shouted, 'Don't, Dad! *Don't*, Dad! Hit *me*, hit *me*!'

Afterwards I swished the terrier, first pointing to the dead cock lying on the floor. When going for walks with me—when he didn't run away—the dog never looked at hens as we passed them. He was a clever dog. When he was watching anything he moved his eyes without moving his head; I could see him thinking. He was like a fox, sly and cunning. I swished him once only before he bit me in the leg, and ran through the nursery door.

To think that I, of all people (I grieved) had come to thrashing a child! I went for an unhappy walk by the river, passing the oak tree under which we had shared so much innocent fancy about an imaginative elf. I felt I could never share such thoughts with my children again.

Walking freed the mind of its condition. I must do something to restore the balance. On my return I found the three sitting on the nursery floor. Windles's railway set was laid out on the carpet, and he was letting the two younger children play with the trains. He was not playing himself, but sitting apart, looking thoughtful. I said I was sorry I had beaten them.

'So you better be!' cried John.

' 'Ee hurt I bad,' said Margaret, her big dark eyes growing shiny with tears, her face reddening, her mouth quivering.

'But you worried me very much, why did you make such a mess? Was it fair to waste the cream like that?'

'Us couldn't help it!' retorted John. 'I didn't mean vor drop the crame bowl, and 'ee wouldn't let Margy go up to the labby, so 'er did'n on the floor.'

'I couldn't help it,' snuffled Margy, putting her hand to her eyes.

'And I was only trying vor clane up th' ole mess, see? Us wasn't sliding!' said John, the more truculently as he saw the look on my face.

Poor Margy! She had tried to tell me what she wanted to do, and I had shouted for her to shut the door. It was entirely my fault.

'I'll tell you what, children. You shall beat me!'

'I won't,' said Margaret.

'I will!' shouted John, and picked up the withy I'd hit the terrier with.

I bent over, touching my toes. John gave me a cut. 'Harder, John!'

'All right!' he giggled.

'Harder, please.'

'Darn, I can't vor strike no harder.'

'Then let Windles try.'

'I won't,' said Windles.

'You can't hurt me,' I retorted.

'All right then!' And he gave me a stinger. I yelped, and hopped, Margy and John laughed. 'More!'

'All right!' said Windles, 'I will this time!'

He did. I pretended to be hurt, hopping and clasping my trousers. Afterwards we were friends in balance again.

A few days later Margaret, coming into my room as I was getting up, said, 'They's the braces you frashed me with, 'tes! They'm sharp. They'm worser than a wasp sting.'

'A wasp sting! Have you been stung, Margy?'

She nodded. 'Harriet Bowden had a bee, and it stinged me. Harriet Bowden was afraid to touch it, and I did and it stinged me.'

She looked at the things on my desk, then out of the window, then after peering up the chimney she said, 'Is there a boss of the world, Dad?'

'What sort of a boss?'

'You know, who has all the houses.'

'Well, all the world is owned by someone or other, I suppose.'

'Yes, but you know, is there a *boss*?'

'One big boss? Only God.'

'He's up in the sky, isn't he? With Jesus? They'm the bosses of the world, ban't 'm?'

'It's questionable.'

'Yes, it be. But Jesus be boss, ban't he?'

'How do you know?'

'Missis Pippacott said so, up to Sunday school.'

Mrs. Pippacott was the farmer's wife, who didn't approve of dancing in the village institute.

'Do *you* go to Sunday school, Margy?'

'Yes, I do.'

'Whatever for?'

'They gives a treat soon.'

'Oh. What do you do there, Margy?'
'Us sings, and the teacher says things.'
'What sort of things do you sing, Margy?'
' 'Tes with the bile-inn.'
'Whatever is a bile-inn?'
'You know, 'tes the tweedle twee thing. You know.'
'A sort of Cold Pudding thing, is it?'
'No, Dad, 'tes the bile-inn, when us sings.'
'Sing now, will you?'
After hesitation and encouragement Margaret sang:

If you see a rainbow in the sky
Pass it on, tweedle twee.

Loetitia told me later that Margy meant violin.
After the treat, Margy went no more to Sunday school.

Galloping Annie had left us before this, and in her place a plump little local cottage woman named Mrs. Ridd worked in the kitchen polishing lamp globes and drying plates and knives and forks, and pushing the pram laden with the Twins, Robbie and Rosie, round the roads for exercise in the afternoon.

Rosie was the daughter of A'Bess, as the children called a friend who was now living with us. A'Bess typed my stories and answered my letters; also she helped me heave rocks about in the river, and fill potato sacks with concrete, for a series of dams I was making. Rosie was born the same week as Robbie, and so, together in one large perambulator, they were called the Twins.

Mrs. Ridd, or Riddy, also had a small daughter, so our cottage nowadays was filled with the noises of children. Windles had made friends with the forester's two sons, and also with the neighbouring farmer's boy, whom we called Sleeboy. I was always glad to see them playing in our cottage, they gave me a feeling of freedom.

And I was glad that Mrs. Ridd worked for us. She was always smiling. Any suggestions about the more efficient scrubbing of floors, stoking of fires, sweeping of flues, chopping of billet wood, etc., were readily and cheerily received. She addressed us all with the old Devon 'my dear', with an extra tenderness to the children, 'dear'ms'. Riddy saw the sense and purpose of what was said to her; and that for me was happiness.

There was something wrong with Baby Robert. At six months he weighed little more than his weight at birth. I used to see him in the kitchen, on Loetitia's or Riddy's or A'Bess's lap, having his napkins changed, and his legs seemed to be no thicker than my thumbs. His wild blue eyes stared up at mine with hostility.

What was I to this mite, with torture in its eyes? What pre-natal *malaise* was in the nerves which contained that essence of life called the soul? Or was it all physical? His mother could not feed him; we could not find food to bring upon him first the candid brow, then the sigh of ease and repletion. All the advertised foods were tried, one after another; he wailed and was thin, they curdled in him and turned sour; he threw them up, our little starveling baby, he who came from a wish to make the wilderness blossom. The blossom was frosty blue as his eyes, speedwell blue, that indefinite blue, not deep and true as of milkwort or gentian, not azure as harebell among the yellowing downland summer grasses, but a wayward frustrate chalky blue. Frowns and screams from the emaciated creature; sudden sweet smile, clear as azure, but so seldom. Spirit of discord incarnate; or merely under-nourishment?

There was nothing wrong with Baby Rosemary. She lay naked in the spring sun, crawling over the grass, plucking and exploring with simian spread of toe. When you picked her up she writhed like an eel, struggling to get on to the grass again. Her hair was bleached white now by the sun and it was time to wean her.

One morning while trying to dictate to A'Bess the story of a farmer I had known, whom so many people called brutal but whom I had always found amiable and intelligent, though obviously from his long inflamed red nose and watery blue eyes his blood-stream was overloaded with acid and even toxic by-products of malnutrition, the grizzling cries of Robbie down below in the garden in his pram suddenly became unendurable. 'Can nothing be done,' I cried, 'obviously the child is starved.'

'He can't keep anything down,' replied A'Bess. 'Loetitia has tried every kind of food, it is always the same, we don't seem able to find what suits him.'

'That baby's dying, why can't he have proper food? Why can't you feed him?' With that Robbie was fetched out of the pram, and glad of the excuse to leave the drudgery of words, I went to the river with my rod.

A week later Robert's weight had increased by one pound, and the gain the second week was a further half-pound. Thereafter he imbibed Savory and Moore's, the favourite food of Windles in the old days at Ham village, and soon became as sturdy as his 'twin'.

As the children grew bigger, the valley became a happier place: although always part of it was in shadow. Ceaselessly the sun rolled over from hill to hill, his work was everlasting. From the gazeless orb of brilliance energy poured down: magnificent to the earth, but a mere dwarf-yellow star of diminishing magnitude in stellar space. It was burning out.

Likewise the human mind, concentrated on one line of thought, was diminishing in energy and light.

Always the river was flowing, by which we walked and watched, and played. Never shall I forget that bright, clear water, into which I gazed from bridge and tree and bank-side, so many thousands of times.

It seemed a long time since Windles and Baby John had first stood by me and watched the trout being turned into the river. How the fish leapt with joy at being free from the confining ice-tanks! They were Scottish trout, from Loch Leven. They were greenish-blue, with black and yellow spots; whereas the native trout in the river were a golden-brown with black and red spots.

When the Loch Leven trout had been living a few weeks in the pool above Humpy Bridge, their yellow spots turned red, and their bluish-green sides became tinged with golden-brown as though they were turning into wild Devon trout. Every day in spring and summer I used to stand on the bridge, and look at them as they lay in the clear water below. The summer sun shining down through the water lit every stone and speck of gravel, every wave of fin and curl of tail, every spot, every crimson opening of a gill-cover as the fish breathed. Each fish had its regular place; it lay on the gravel, always head to stream, watching the water before and beside it for food floating down. The biggest fish had the best place; the next biggest had the next best place.

The natural food of the trout were the flies which hatched out of the water—not buzzing flies of the kind which bite or sting or are a nuisance in the house, but beautiful, gauzy-winged creatures which lived only a brief while, laid their eggs on the water at evening, and then fell spent, to float away, their brief aerial life over. In time the eggs they dropped out of their long slender tri-forked tails, or whisks, hatched, and became tiny creatures crawling on the gravel, some building themselves homes of sand-speck and bits of leaf and twig, others hiding in the water-mosses and feeding on the little vegetables which grow on the gravel. These vegetables were very small, and looked, to my eyes, as I knelt by the river bank, like a thin brown slime on the stones, but to the creatures they were what a pasture is to grazing cattle. After living about a year under water, the creatures turn into nymphs, which swim up to the surface, break out of their cases, and arise, very tremulously, as winged flies of the stream. They are frail, delicate, fairy-like things, and live but a few hours. Often in summer I watched them dancing over the water as the sun was setting—they rose and fell as they dropped their eggs, dipping in the water and flying up again—until a ripple broke, and became a ring, and a trout had risen to take one.

I used to feel sad when I thought of these lovely, dream-like creatures dying in the sunset of their one day of life, but after watching the river for a long time, and seeing how all life renewed itself, how the salmon returned from the sea and laid their eggs in the gravel, and died, and the little salmon hatched and fed on the nymphs, and went down to the sea, and returned again to the river of their ancestors—spring, summer, autumn, winter, season after season like a wheel turning slowly round, the great stars of heaven wheeling in eternity—it seemed to me, when I had watched this wheel of life turning, always the same complete turn every year, that all life and death made up the beauty of the river, which had flowed through the valley thousands of centuries before the children and I walked under the hills, holding hands and laughing and peering at the strange life of the river—the beautiful, limpid, shadow-dreaming Bray—the stream which would be flowing a thousand centuries after we were all forgotten.

Day after day of sunshine we stood on Humpy Bridge and threw spoonfuls of food into the pool, and watched the trout coming down like torpedoes, each with its little bow-wave, and saw them slashing round with open mouths to take the food with heads upstream. Always they feed upstream, for the water has to be poured through the gills for a fish to breathe. Therefore a trout faces upstream, not only to watch for its natural food coming down, but for the flow of water to pass through its gills. How they leapt and splashed, under the showers of food! Big trout and little trout, samlets and even eels, all came to the daily banquet. The curious thing was that while this food—which was like broken-up dog biscuit meal—made the wild brown trout look like the greenish Loch Leven fish, the natural fly-food in the river made the Loch Levens resemble the native brownies! How did that happen? Obviously the colour of the spots came from the kind of food the trout ate. Indeed, some of the Loch Levens, which went on upstream and lived entirely wild, looked after a few months exactly like the golden-brown, scarlet-spotted natives! Only by their shape could we tell the difference.

Windles was five when our first tame trout were put into the pool. He used to lead Baby John by the hand across the deer park, following me, and Baby John used to stand by the stone-coping and always, his eyes wide and solemn, point towards the railway viaduct a mile up the valley and lisp, 'Sheed-er-shish? Dad-dad go sheed-er-shish?' He was too small to look over into the river, and one day as we stood there he became very excited, and said, 'Look, sheed-er-shish!' and lo, his idea of feeding the fish was a goods train passing on the viaduct of the Great Western Railway.

A year later John was just big enough to look over the bridge, when standing on a special stone placed there for him. The fish remained in the pool during the winter floods, when the water ran too heavy and fast for us to feed them. They became thin, but soon fattened again when spring brought nymphs and flies and showers of food from the familiar figures on the bridge. Sometimes a salmon lived with them awhile, aloof and solitary, never feeding, waiting for the autumn and the spawning season, when its eggs would be laid. I used to see Windles and John creeping over Humpy Bridge, heads down, slowly to peer over into the water below. A fourth pair of eyes was trying to look over when another spring came round —Baby Margaret, led there by John while Windles was at school. John used to grasp Baby Margaret round the middle, and struggle and strain to heave her up on the stone so that she could see Daddy's Tame Shishes. These trout were now three, four, and even five times as big as they had been when we put them in the river. Always we missed one or two when a new spring came, and we returned to feed them. New, smaller trout took their place—their children perhaps.

A heron speared the biggest fish one year, and we found it dying in the shallows. Perhaps otters took others. The little fingerlings of one year became the big ones two or three years later. Time flowed away as the water; it was always Now, always the same river, always the trout were there, waiting below for the showers of food during the summer.

And then Margaret was leading Baby Robert to the bridge to see the fish. Sometimes Rosemary came too; and five small heads were peering over as the spoonfuls were cast upon the waters.

Afterwards the children would undress in the sunlight, and with shrill cries of joy and excitement would splash about at the edge of the stream, while I lay still in the shallow water, on the golden gravel of the ford, watching the clear cold water foaming over my body, watching it whirling the sand-specks and scooping the stones in little waterfalls and eddies along my length, feeling myself and the children part of the great stream of life, and deeply content for the gift of being alive in the world.

But, alas, house life was not so easy as when the sun shone down on us. I was now Father, with a capital F.

'Be quiet, babies, silence, I say! Our Father's thinking!' hissed Windles, frowning terrifically upon them.

The cottage, which had seemed so spacious when first we went there, was now too small. The sitting-room and the day nursery led one into another through a door with upper panels of glass. Once when I was sitting by the hearth, wondering what to do with myself, I saw five faces peering at me through the glass, two small faces at one end, or rather eyes and foreheads, above finger-tips pressing there. They vanished! Father must not be disturbed. 'Damn Father!' I said.

In the open air, my restrictions fell away; and I became, thank heaven, Arkernoo, a person who provided all kinds of unexpected excitement. Arkernoo was a name originally invented by Rosie, and copied by the other children. Perhaps Windles, and his friend Sleeboy, son of Farmer Slee, Dolly Ridd, John, and Margy, Harriet Bowden, Rosie, Robbie, and others, would be playing in the deer park, and the car would appear with the trailer hitched on behind, to get wood from one or another of the cords under the trees.

'Come on, get in, everyone!'

'Hurray, Arkernoo's come, now for some sporty behaviour!' cried Windles.

'Coo, I bet we whizz!' said John, pink-cheeked with quiet excitement.

'Yes, us'll whizz, now won't us, Rosie?' echoed Robert.

'Yes, us'll whizz now, won't us, Robbie?'

Across the grass the trailer swayed with its laughing, shouting cargo, and, coming to a smooth place, where no ant-hills were, would accelerate, and go round and round faster and faster until all were shrieking with laughter. Or the engine would be stopped and the children chased; or a football match organized, and the wood forgotten. Father, thank God, was forgotten; I was one of them, I had got back, for a while, to the land of enchantment, of unself-consciousness, to the world of otters, deer, salmon, water, moonshine, and Cold Pudding—the only world in which perhaps there was consistency, form, integrity. Back again in the house, with letters, bills, and typescripts, the ever-pressing need to turn feelings into words, this world too often faded, and the children were problems of noise, dirt, and even irritation; but never of resentment.

One evening of early summer, when I returned to the

cottage after trouting, the boys cried out that they had a baby Tarka. They had found it outside a field drain in the deer park, and had carried it home in a handkerchief.

A glance showed that the small, sinuous, brave-sly-eyed animal was no otter, but a stoat. The tip of its inch-long tail was dark brown, distinguishing it from weasel. It was scarcely weaned. Its milk-teeth were not yet hard. It made a shrill chattering cry. Probably its mother had been trapped by one of the keepers, and it had wandered out in its hunger.

The boys declared it to be an otter cub. Mother had said so. Farmer had said so. Their minds resisted readjustment. I said I thought it was a stoat; a little Swagdagger, not a baby Tarka.

'Oh, I love it!' cried Windles, aged seven, ecstatically.

'Better put it back where you found it.'

'Oh, I do love it!'

Half seriously I gave it the worst character: a blood-sucker; bird-strangler; gnawer of rabbits' eyes; eater of living flesh only.

'But God made it,' retorted Windles.

'How do you know God made it?'

'You told me when I was four that God made trout and otters, so I thought God must have made this too,' he replied. When sure that we were not laughing at him, but at me, he dared (being a very sensitive child) to ask again if he might keep it. Might he, please? Certainly, if he wanted to. He could always do what he liked.

It became for the children the Dear One. After their bath they came down in pyjamas to peer into the inverted barrel and say good night to it, where it lay curled in cotton-wool beside a saucer of milk and bread. Such a darling little thing, wasn't it, Dad? Such sweet little paws and face, hadn't it, Mum? Windles hugged himself with joy. The next night it nipped his finger; he looked bewildered, then he scowled with mortification at the betrayal of his benevolent feelings, and gave the stoat to his brother aged four.

The beast did not thrive. Occasionally I saw it trying to eat. It chittered much, calling its parents. It was ill. Obviously it had been injured when they brought it home. I thought it would die soon of peritonitis; unless the Parson Jack Russell terrier, expert mouse-snapper, secret-sly chicken-slayer, got it first. The terrier, at every opportunity, and despite threats and thwacks of every kind, dashed to the inverted barrel whenever he saw a chance.

Hearing or smelling the dog, the infant stoat would raise its long flat head, the shape of a hawk's skull, and remain poised. It showed no fear. Weak, starved, soon to die, it did not cower or flinch, but waited with head upheld in the enemy's direction.

Seeing its plight, Windles reclaimed it. We fed it on warm milk from an old fountain-pen filler. We wrapped it in cotton-wool. He was heard praying at night for its recovery. Secretly, in the tenderest tones, while leaning cautiously over the barrel rim, he exhorted the Dear One to live.

The fourth evening the terrier, whom no threat could daunt, got into the barrel. We hurried to the sounds of thumping, shoving, scrambling, chittering. He was lugged out and hurled away. There by the overturned saucer and crushed box stood the stoat, its head still upheld, but swaying on its neck. In the morning it was curled on its side, a mite hardly big enough to fill the palm of the hand, languid with the chills of approaching death. I carried it in my trouser pocket, but soon 'it was a-go', as the old people said of death in the West Country.

The face of Windles appeared round the door, his eyes wet with unhappiness. He would kill the dog. But why? God also made the dog. Oh, did God? The boy ran away, and hid; was observed shaking his fist at the sky; told his mother he would say no more prayers.

Later when we buried the Dear One under a rose tree Windles became tranquil when it was suggested that he would perhaps see his friend again in a different form, but under the same sky. And the next day all seemed to be forgotten.

The terrier was incorrigible, and killed more chickens. So I gave him away to a pack of foxhounds. There Chico was so quarrelsome that the hounds, each many times his weight, became afraid of him. Even the stallion hound seemed to lose confidence in Chico's presence. This is not really surprising, since the terrier had been bred of a line of earth-dogs chosen for their courage in facing a badger underground, not merely to yap from a distance of two feet, as the grey tore at soil and stones to get away from its human enemies digging down to its pipe. A terrier that will bite into the jowl of a brock or grey and hold to its bite despite ripping claw-strokes and the twistings of a powerful neck to free its jaw for that dreaded double lock which could bite bones to splinters is rare.

After Chico had mastered the hounds, he pinned one of the huntsman's horses by the fetlock, and so was put down.

5

Nature, and Some Natural History

As they grew older, I saw how different the children were. John was the easiest-going. He was seldom put out, always adaptable. At seven years he was long-haired, soft-voiced, wide-eyed, ever ready to help anyone do anything. Solemnly he made cakes in the kitchen—real cakes, not mud-pies or mere hardened lumps of dough—or laid the dinner-table, helping with the washing-up, writing his book of twenty-six chapters (*About my Life*, by John Williamson, which appears later in this story) and tending his garden (three feet by two feet). He helped make the beds, he took Rosie and Robbie for walks, he knitted a pair of socks for Sleeboy's baby brother, he held the net for me while I threw a fly up-stream under the alders. Wouldn't he rather go away and play with the other boys? It must be dull for him waiting about while a water-absorbed fisherman, with cat-like intentness, moved so slowly upstream, casting a red gamecock-hackle fly foot by foot higher in the runs and eddies. Oh no, said John, he liked carrying the net, he liked looking in the grass and seeing ants and spiders and 'other fings'. He was quietly happy, enjoying whatsoever he was doing.

Windles was restless, impetuous, imaginative. He was always making up scenes and actions in his mind, living a life other than that which was around him at the moment. But plenty of exercise kept him healthy. It is overmuch mental study, the bodily inaction of so-called culture and education, which is the *malaise* of civilized life.

When John and Margaret were little they used to play together in the nursery, and like all small things, whether puppies or otter cubs or children, used to struggle one with the other. Usually it was over toys. Margaret was the stronger. Every struggle was a deadlock; both had an equal grip on toy and hair. There they sat, the fair-haired, thin-bodied John looking faintly flushed and a little surprised and hurt, while Margy showed her teeth in rage, her dark hair—or that part of it not in her brother's grip—falling over her brown eyes and gipsy cheeks. With a gruff roar of 'What's all this about, hey? hey? hey? hey?' Father would shake them together, or perhaps pretend to be getting ready to beat John, when Margy, baring her teeth, would try and pull John away to safety. After the personal release against the common enemy, what was the cause of the trouble? Maybe it was Margy's bedtime, and she was fretful; or John needed a drink of lemonade. Or barley sugar, perhaps? The principle in our house was that there were never any naughty children. There were tired children, there were frustrated children, there were ill-fed children; but never any naughty children.

I remember being surprised, and somehow pleased, when one day I heard Loetitia say to John, who was trailing after her and grizzling a little, 'Don't you whine to me, my boy!' Her affection never became sentimentality.

Robert was very nearly a problem-child. How he asked questions! And, being put off, how easily his manner became defiance. As he was usually put off—toys not belonging to him being taken away—'Robert, don't do that! Robert, shut up! Oh damn you, Robert! Clear off! Come on Robbie, bedtime! Robbie, don't throw your food on the floor! Robert, come out of the water! Robert, get out of Father's car! Robert, stop making that row, our Father's working!'—Robert's dominant manner was a protesting defiance. Almost invariably he did things by opposites. When I heard him being carried downstairs in the morning, I sometimes gave a whistle—a keen high note, for penetrating noise. Robbie's instant reaction would be, 'I ban't gwin' to say good morning, you nasty ole Daddy!' So to get him to do anything I used to ask him to do the opposite thing. Next morning it was, 'Don't say good morning, will you, Robbie, I'm a nasty old Daddy.'

'You ban't a nasty ole Daddy, tho'!'

'No, I'm not, am I?'

"YES, YOU BE!' he would yell.

A gash is as painful to one as an amputation to another, wrote Francis Thompson, *pour a puddle into a thimble, or an Atlantic in Etna, both puddle and mountain overflow.* Robert went white in the face when bed was mentioned at 11 a.m. in the morning. His blue eyes dimmed with anguish, for leaving the intense delights of the imaginary world he was torn away from. He would cry out; then, finding himself captive and overpowered, would weep. I knew that anguish, ah yes, I knew. For all the children were part of me, part of what I had been, what I had suffered and delighted in, as a child. So I took him away to my room, and let him please himself, when his voice became soft and happy. He wrapped himself in the sheep-skin rugs on my camp-bed, and played with my wooden toys from the Pyrenees, or the Black Forest, and the worried white look would disappear, blue colour come back into his eyes, as he did just what he liked—the mite wearing the other children's discarded clothes.

Every morning he came to my room to give his coo-coo a rest, and the kip-kip its hay. The coo-coo was a bit battered, without horns, and minus one leg, and the little lead horse had a hole in its side, and no legs at all—but Robbie loved them, and went upstairs happily because they were tired; and hadn't Robbie himself known what it was to feel tired? Robbie had seen Farmer Slee's kip-kip and coo-coo both needed to have a rest sometime.

So with a fragment clutched in each hand, Farmer Robert took them up to his farm, which was my bed.

There was happiness for this wayward child when Rosemary was staying in the house. Rosie and Robbie loved one another. When Rosie went away with A'Bess to London, Robert would walk about the house and the garden, asking when Rosie was coming back. When she did return he brought her armfuls of his toys, his face alight with joy. Robert was like Windles, but more sensitive. When happy, free, himself, his face shone with eager light; he seemed bodyless: Ariel. Say to Robbie, 'Once upon a time—' and dream would come into the blue eyes, the mouth would open, and Robbie would stand, waiting to be enchanted. I would not let them cut his hair, which lay on his shoulders in yellow curls.

I loved his long yellow hair and blue eyes, he was a little Viking of dream, so sweet and wild.

Robert said No per-lay when he meant 'yes'. John

patiently tried to teach him to say yes. Robert would repeat, yes.

'That's right, good little boy, Robbie. Now I'll ask you, would you like an apple?'

'Six!' promptly replied Robert, meaning he wanted two, one for each hand.

'No, what I mean was—er, well, I'll tell 'ee, would 'ee like six apples, Robbie?'

'No per-lay!' cried Robert, ecstatically; and wept when he found that after all there were no apples in the house.

What was it Robert used to call a hot-water bottle? When going to bed at night he demanded six—one for each hand—'six hot-wa'r bottoms'. Riddy must carry him up to his cot, always Riddy. Only Riddy was allowed to give him intimate, personal service. Once I volunteered to aid him; and oh! the surprising words shouted at me! He had been vaccinated against small-pox; and now against using obscene words in later life. It was always pleasing to hear very small boys using such words—they didn't use them in our house after three or four years of age.

The last time Robbie swore was on his third birthday. To Cousin Mary, he shouted, seeing her for the first time, 'You ban't staying yurr in this house very long, you dirty old cow!' Only the word wasn't cow. Cousin Mary, having small boys of her own, met this affront with equanimity, and said she was sorry, indeed. To which a contrite Robert replied, 'No, you can stay, you be a *clean* old cow, ban't you, my dear?'

Mrs. Ridd, smiling and jolly, was romantic. She read twopenny weekly romantic magazines, with such titles as *The Miracle*, and *Love Tales*. 'Oh, I loves me books, I'd die without they!' she would say, with a cheerful smile. Then 'Lovely li'l boy Robbie be, ban't 'm midear? Oh, I loves that li'l maid, Rosie, tew, so quick, so bright 'er be!'

Windles was teaching himself to use a typewriter, having been shown by A'Bess the purpose of the various levers. The first thing he did was to type out a list of books for Riddy. I kept the list, and here it is, just as typed:

Fol. 99
Mrs. Ridd *Shallowford* *Devon*

Bought of Windles Williamson	£	s.	d.
The Gold Falcon		7	6
Seven Pillars of Wisdom		30	–
Winged Victory		7	6
Tarka the Otter		7	6
1 leg of lamb		6	8
2 lb. Pork Sausages		3	6
Total		10	2

John also learned to type; indeed during this year, the sixth in the valley of the Bray, when he was away from school for the summer term because he was pale and thin and must live in the sun, he wrote his autobiography.

I asked him to write a chapter every day, telling him only that he should write the truth, for that was the best kind of writing. That was the only help he got from me. John's book shall have a chapter to itself later on. The style is direct and terse, English-biblical.

One afternoon about half-past three I saw John and Margaret slinking along at the bottom of the swamp. Each had a loaf under one arm, and Margy also carried a bottle. Seeing me, they broke into a run and hid behind the faggot heap. I followed them, and they ran to the greenhouse. They had taken the loaf from Riddy's cottage porch, where it awaited collection by her mother, and had filled a sauce bottle with water, pretending it was milk.

At first I felt unhappy that my children should steal; and being as it were *occluded* in mind, for awhile, in thought at least, reacted like 'any Victorian parent' (my own, that is) and wondered if this were the beginning of a life of dishonesty, even of crime. It is laughable now: but for an hour or so on that spring day it was depressing. It also gave me an insight into the worries of an older generation. Soon, thank goodness, the incident came into balance: except that I was obviously in danger of emotional intolerance, for that I could be put out by a mere adventurous escapade of two small children and 'order them to go to bed'. And to crown my folly, I ordered John to type out a confession.

To ease his soul, I thought: whereas it was my soul that needed easement.

Me and margaret stole to loves of bread at

> first we eat little bit and then ran in the green house and eat the little bits. And then i told margaret to steel the to loves of. Bread when we where run-ing daddy saw us run-ing. with the 2 loves of bread and then daddy ran up the path and coot hold of margaret and took her indoors. And told me to go get the other love of bread and of warter and then we went to Bed but we only stade in bed a-bout four a-clock and drest when we where in bed daddy came up and hit me with some sticks and then I Siad margaret it doesnt hart i siad to margaret. daddy was play-ing with the sticks, then daddy told us that it was granny rids bread.

Meanwhile Robert was sitting in his high chair in the kitchen, happily beating his spoon on the tray before him, or occupied in tearing up books and news-papers. 'All lies! All lies!' he cried.

Riddy gave him her wedding ring to wear, and when he saw me, Robbie said in his high, quick voice, his words tumbling over each other with eagerness, 'I—I—I'll tell 'ee suthin'! I be in a cage with Riddy!' holding up the ring on his finger; and Mrs. Ridd would exclaim, 'My dear soul, what ideas the chiel do have!' and double herself with laughing, for she had been pretending she was *engaged* to Robbie.

John later said to her, quite seriously, 'Be 'ee married to Mr. Ridd?'

'For why, Jannie?'

'Ooh, I dunno.' Then, 'I thought I'd marry 'ee myself one day—only not in Filleigh church, you knaw!'

Soon after Robbie asked Margy to be his sweetheart,

then changed his mind and told us he had married himself to John.

Robbie had curious ideas about words. When he yelled *Good night Good night Good night!* or rather *Goo nate goo nate goo nate!* it meant he wanted a cup of milk. For Windles, milk used to be *Bookadink*; for John it was *Ke'l boilin'*; for Margy, just plain *Mook*.

While the elder boys were in school, Margy sometimes used to come and see me in my writing-room, where I encouraged her to talk to me. Windles and John called her 'Maggot'; their attitude to her generally was one of scorn and dismissal. Loetitia told me that Margy suffered because of it, and would I try and counter it? So I made a friend of Margy, with her wide-mouthed and half-shy grin, and when I sat her on my lap and put my arms round her she used to press herself against me and almost I could hear the purring of her warm and responsive nature.

For some years the rotting section of a beech tree lying in the deer park by the river had reminded me constantly that one day I must bring an iron bar and heave it into the water. I must also bring wire-rope, my wooden beetel made from a section of an old apple-tree trunk I had thrown in the garden, and some oak pegs, and so anchor the log in the gravel, otherwise the next spate would take it down to the Atlantic.

The log was about nine feet long and two feet thick. Because it was unsuitable for the sawmills, the axemen and timber-wagon crew had left it lying there after felling timber about ten years previously. Anchored on the shallows, it would be a refuge for water-snails and other trout food. In a moorland stream the gravel is often shifted by floods, and then the jelly-like egg-sacs of snails are ground up and destroyed. A log sunken and fixed to the river bed would be a nursery of small insect and other aquatic life. Also it would make a nice eddy wherein to throw a fly.

'Why do 'ee want vor put'n in the river, Dad?' inquired Margaret, beside me.

With tools in wheelbarrow we went along the river bank, to shift the log into the water.

'To make a hidey place for a trout,' I replied.

'For my breakfast,' she announced. 'Nice daddy,' and rubbed the side of her head against my pocket.

The log was not so heavy as I had thought. Dry-rot and other fungi had eaten most of its heart away. On top it was sodden, but the first heave with the iron bar rolled it over, with tearing noises of grass roots.

A run of little tunnels lay exposed in the hollow of earth wherein the log had bedded itself. 'What be they li'l pits, Dad?'

'They're the runs of voles, cousins to mice, Margy. They've got browny red coats and short tails.'

'Yes, they have, haven't 'm, Dad?'

Beside one gallery lay a ball of dry bitten grasses. The top of the ball had lifted away with the log, exposing the interior of the voles' home. And what luck for us! Two mice lay there. I could see their heads. I whispered to Margy that they were asleep.

'Yes, Dad, they be cuddling one another, ban't 'm?'

That was exactly what the voles were doing. Their forepaws were round each other's neck.

As I peered, an eye like an elderberry opened. A whiskered head looked up. The eye blinked. A nose flaired delicately. Whiskers twitched. The other head looked up.

Two mouths opened simultaneously in a yawn. Then, aware that something had happened, necks were hastily unclasped, they stared about them, at the ruin of their thatched roof, at the brightness of the winter sky.

I heard the child gasp, and turning round, saw a snake slowly uncoiling from a dry hole in the log. It was an adder, a thin lanky sort of viper, the markings on its back much faded. I felt a surge of horror in me, although I knew it was torpid with winter sleep.

Meanwhile one of the mice had hopped out of the grass ball. It was surprisingly fat for a mouse that slept so much. There was a heap of bitten beech-mast near the ball.

Margy cowered against me, for the snake was trying to move along the earth. But it was a sleepy snake; it stopped, and after yawning, swayed its head drowsily. Its eyes were half-gummed up.

The March sun shone weakly, and we watched, while the second mouse climbed out of the nest and sat shivering beside the other mouse. I was in two minds about killing the snake. But in summer it would slither, swift and rustling, through the hot grass, where a small naked brown foot, with broad spreading toes, might be pressing. And then. . . .

While I was trying to make up my two minds, Margy whispered again, 'Dad, look, what be thaccy!' She was pointing at a dark brown nose poking out between dead beech leaves in a sort of alcove of the log. I touched it with my stick, and the ball fell solidly on the grass. It lay there, unmoving.

'It's a furze-pig, or hedge-boar, Margy. Look, it's rolled itself in leaves, for a blanket, before going to sleep for the winter.'

Hedgehogs, I whispered to her, ate snakes, nipping them by the tail before curling up and waiting while the snake beat itself to death on its spines.

'The furze-pig is probably rather hungry, Margy.'

'Yes, it prob'ly is rather hungry, Dad, ban't it?'

'Shall us give the snake to it for its dinner, Margy?'

She nodded. 'Then th' vuzz-peg won't be no more hungry, will it, Dad?'

'But what about the poor snake, Margy? What about its children?' I put a false pathos into my words.

'That poor snake will cry if it don't see its children no more, won't it, Dad?'

'Well, certainly it won't like being eaten.'

'No, it won't, will it, Dad? Us mustn't let the nasty ole vuzz-peg eat the poor snake, must us?'

'But the snake might eat the mice, Margy. Aren't the mice pretty, Margy? Do you remember your "ghose"?'

'Oh yes, Dad, I love my ghose! They be dear little mouses, ban't 'm? Us won't kill the mouses, will us, Dad? Us won't tell the boys, or they might kill the mouses, mightn't 'm, Dad?'

'But supposing the nasty old snake sees the poor mice, Margy, and feeling hungry, wants to eat them?'

'Us mustn't let the nasty old snake eat the mouses, us must kill the snake, mustn't us, Dad?'

'But look, Margy, if the vuzz-peg unrolls himself, he will see the snake, and kill it, won't he? Then us needn't kill it.'

'No, us won't kill it, will us, Dad! The vuzz-peg will want to kill it for 'isself, won't he?'

'But then the poor snake won't see his children any more, will he?'

'No, Dad, he won't.'

'Then shall us kill the nasty old vuzz-peg, Margy?'

'Yes, Dad, kill it.'

'What, kill poor old frightened Prickleboy, Margy?'

'No, us mustn't kill poor Prickleboy, must us, Dad?'

'Then what shall we kill, Margaret?'

'Us'll kill nought, shall us, Dad?' adding in a warning voice, possibly acquired during her three recent voluntary visits, entirely out of curiosity and also to show off her new patent leather party shoes, to the chapel Sunday school in the village, 'else God might kill us, mightn't He, Dad?'

How easy it was to prejudice the children's minds!

How easy, too, to upset their natural balance of feelings, and make dominant, for example, the sense of pity.

Windles came home from school in the twilight carrying something carefully in his hands. 'Look!' he cried, with a kind of possessive triumph in his voice. He held out a shoddy bundle of feathers from which depended white legs with clenched claws and lolling head. It was a barn, or white owl; dead. Its eyes were glazed and shrunken.

'Did anyone shoot it?'

'I don't know. I found it just like that, in the deer park, lying on the grass,' he replied, a little anxiously.

'He wants to know if he can have it stuffed,' said Loetitia, gently in my ear.

Taking it in the hand for examination, the first thing one noticed was its extreme lightness. Although the barn owl in flight looks twice, and in some lights, thrice the size of a pigeon, its body is not larger than a pigeon's. The pigeon is a fast-flying bird, with tight feathers; the white owl fans slowly over the mice-runs in the grass and around the ricks and faggot piles. The pigeon's flight quills are hard and narrow; the owl's broad and soft, fringed with filaments of down which wave in the least breath of air.

They are the silencers of flight; an owl beating down the hedge at sunset is not heard even by mice. It has a moth-like softness, hovering and fanning with large dark eyes in a heart-shaped face peering down; the wings close and the softness becomes a powerful grip of talons. Mice are swallowed whole, after being killed with claw and beak. Later, bones and fur in a casting, or pellet, are ejected from the owl's crop.

Now how had this owl died? It had not been shot, its wings were not broken, its breast was white, although draggled. But how light it was, held in the hand, a few ounces only, a feathered skeleton.

'Look, Windles, at its legs. They're broken.'

The legs were about two and a half inches long, covered with short hairs of incipient feathers like silver wire. One leg appeared to be broken in the thigh. It was withered. The foot of the other leg was maimed; one of the toes was missing. The wound was half-healed. The bird had died of starvation, after struggling in and escaping from a rabbit gin.

Standing with my little boy in the lane, the owl between us, I gave him an imaginary picture of its life since it had escaped from the gin. At first, wild fright and freedom; crooked and tottery perching on an oak branch; falling off; a rest spread-winged in the grass below. Pain, bewilderment, glancing about in the grass for an unknown enemy. An owl's eyes were fixed, it could turn its head a whole circle on its neck. Hunger, and after a painful take-off, to the air again. A mouse moving below; descent and grip upon the shadow; the mouse escaping. The owl falling over, and flapping upright on useless feet, bewildered.

A very hungry owl would seek its barn or hollow tree, there to stare in pain throughout daylight, its great ears, hid under feathers, hearing the movements of woodlice, shrews, even worms in the leaf-mould below. At sunset it would flap out laboriously and fly along its regular evening ways.

It would catch no mice. Always it would fall over as it tried to grip them, and flap upright again, and stare about it.

There were no beetles or moths in the grass of winter. It would begin to feel cold, in spite of its feathers.

At night the flashes of the Dogstar above our valley seemed to liquefy in the north wind pouring from the high ground of Exmoor. Perhaps that thin skirling cry we heard coming from the direction of the farmer's haystack a night or two before, when the constellations were so big and bright, was the death-cry of this bird.

'We saw an owl flying strangely, do you remember, Winny? Wan and irresolute in the wind it passed, a white blur drifting and swaying, we saw it from your bedroom window, do you remember? The starlight made Farmer Slee's haystack and the hedge very clear. Perhaps the owl did not see the stars, for death is a darkening of the sight, the world fading away. On it flew, tumbling blindly and crying, to fall in the grass, and sleep away from the cold and the pain, until you found it and brought it home, this poor little ghost of a bird. Ah no, boy, it isn't fair to make you cry. Let's all go for a walk on Santon Sands to-morrow! All of us! It's Saturday, no school tomorrow, hurray! Shall we, Windles? John, Margy, how about a walk tomorrow?'

'Shut up,' says Windles. Then, 'I don't want the owl. John can have it.'

'Coo, can I? *Thanks*, Windles.'

'No, Windles ought to get it stuffed,' I said. 'It's our family totem, the owl, and the eldest son shall have it to hang over his bed, with wings in flight. It will keep the rats out of your bed,' I said to Windles. 'Ha ha ha,' replied Windles, with hollow laughter.

The wind was rising; and in the night a gale blew in from the sea. All the better for our walk on the morrow!

6

We Go Travelling

And what a sight greeted our eyes as we came down the path by the sandstone cliffs of Santon, overlooking the Burrows, that miniature desert by the estuary of the Two Rivers! When we reached the shore we saw that hundreds, thousands, of oranges had been cast up by the storm. Like yellow beads they lay along the tide-line, among bottles, seaweed, crab-shells, feathers of gulls and curlews, branches and roots of trees, broken crab-pots, and ominously, six straw palliasses or mattresses all together. The irregular line of tide-wrack lay at the foot of the sandhills, cast there by the last waves of the high tide driven before a south-west No. 8 wind.

When the children first saw the oranges, they ran forward, and grabbed them. Having pushed one into each trouser pocket, John and Windles began to stuff their jerseys with them. Margaret held two in her hands, while vainly trying to conceal another in the pocket of her skirt, which her mother had sewn there to hold a very small handkerchief. Once again she learned that it was much better to be a boy. She returned slowly. 'My pocket ban't no gude at all,' she said, near to tears.

I rolled one down the wet firm sand. She threw one

too; then, with the impulse to share a delight, she ran crying to the boys to tell them to roll all the oranges down the sand. Along the next half-mile of shore the children had much fun with them, evolving and discarding in succession various forms of hand and foot games.

'Look, John, you throw one up in the air, and try and hit it with another one, like this. Look, John! Watch! John!'

'All right. Coo! Look, Win, if you kick one hard it busts, ever so sploshy, look, Win.'

'All right, only let's play football, shall we? When I pass to you, you must pass it back, like at school, see. Only don't keep the ball too long. Pass! Come on, pass! John, damn you, pass! Half-wit! You're no good.' John had kicked air, and fallen over.

Windles played by himself.

'Windles, let's throw some down towards those gulls, and see if they fly up, or if they will know it is only an orange. Now then, both together.'

The gulls merely walked away, regarding the rolling spheres with watchful suspicion.

'Daddy, can't we sell them? People won't know they be bad, they don't look bad, do 'm?'

'Oh, John, you crook!'

'Crook yourself. I'll take some to school, and chuck 'em at the chaps, I will. And at you, too, old Daddy Wee!'

'Dad, us must take one to Baby Robert, mustn't us, for Baby Robert be too small to come today, ban't 'm!'

'Yes, ban't 'm?' mocked John. 'Can't speak proper, you can't!'

But Margy didn't care, now she was holding her father's hand.

'So be you,' she retorted.

'Was there a wreck, do you think, Dad? John, you fool, don't throw that rotten fruit at Margaret. I'll chuck one at you, and hard, if you do!'

'I don't trouble.'

I hurled an orange hard on the sand, to burst it. Fashion followed; changed. Soon oranges were being hurled at boots and shoes. But at last even the boys were weary of oranges. Tens of thousands lay along the tide-line. One only had been nibbled by a rat, who appeared to have found it uneatable. All were spoiled by the salt. By their size and shape they looked to be Florida oranges.

We wondered if the cargo boat had been wrecked. How had they been packed: loose or in crates, asked Windles. For if they had been loose, then surely the boat had foundered, he said. And those straw mattresses, were they from the boat too? Far out in the bay, to 'Lundy high, sign of dry', the white rollers were in turmoil.

From Padstow Point to Lundy light
Is a watery grave by day and by night.

'I don't want to be a sailor,' said Windles, looking at the grey sea.

John had a sudden idea. 'Some greedy man bought them and threw them away because they'm bad.'

'Yes,' said Margaret. 'Some greedy man bought them because they'm bad, and that greedy man threw them—'

'Ha ha ha!' Windles shouted with laughter.

'Half-wit!' shouted John, pink in the face. 'I didn't say because 'm bad, I said so-so-so-so-some m-m-m-man bought 'm, do you see, I said because he wanted to—I said, WHY DON'T YOU LISTEN?' shouted John, his eyes bright as a weasel's, in stuttering rage.

'You did say that, then!' retorted Margaret. Tactlessly, grinning, 'Didn't he, Dad?'

'Stool pigeon,' said Windles.

'So be you!'

'Maggot!'

'So be you!'

There was a large collection of glossy seaweed on the sand by us, and I pushed over all three upon it. They picked themselves up and began to bombard me, common enemy for the moment, while the gulls, birds without any sense of fun, living all their lives in competition for food, huddled immobile on the sands below, may have wondered what it was all about.

I enjoyed that expedition so much that a few Saturdays later we set out again. It was Margy's fifth birthday and for her treat we planned to go to Lynmouth for the day, where among other things a prominent notice-board said:

Shelley's Cottage

Bed and Breakfast

The miniature railway from Barum to Lynton would soon be closed, for few used it at that time. The journey took twice as long as the omnibus, though the little railway was four times as nice to travel on. The children had never travelled on the train, so it would be their first and last time.

Margaret, John, Windles, his friend Sleeboy, A'Bess, and I stood on the platform at the beginning of our journey and inspected the miniature engine.

'Cor, look at the big funnel,' said John.

'I say, look Sleeboy, it's got a cow-catcher, but I suppose it's for the red deer, and what a huge dome—I bet it takes the driver a long time to polish it every morning,' said Windles, whose job it was every Saturday to shine the brass door handles at home.

Margaret touched my hand. 'Look, Dad, isn't it lovely.' She pointed to a baby in one of the carriages. Her only doll was broken some months ago.

We climbed into the last coach. The whistle blew a high comic note and, by the rattling, fussy noises, we were soon travelling at a great rate. Yet the railings and walls of the wharfside buildings of Rolle quay were passing very slowly. I put my feet up on the seat before me, and sighed happily, relaxed.

'Cor, 'er's stopped, 'er's used up all the steam!' cried John, disappointment in his voice, as we stood at Snapper Halt, a few minutes later.

'On the contrary, at any moment 'er may bust,' I said. Certainly the engine was wreathed in what appeared to be an excessive volume of steam. 'But perhaps the driver's only stoking her up for a cup of tea.'

'Don't talk rot, Dad,' scoffed Windles, then seeing my face, 'Is it true?'

'Well, I remember the driver of the French troop train which took us up the line to St. Omer in 1914, giving us water to make tea with in our mess tins.'

The next carriage was filled with schoolgirls. 'Let's scare them, by pretending to have a fight,' suggested Windles. So we shouted and banged about. A scream like a bantam cock's came from the engine. Rattle, shake, jig. We were off again; past Chelfham with its high viaduct, and up the valley, leaving the little Yeo stream far below.

'I hope there's lots to eat, I'm hungry, I am,' said John, staring at the rusty, empty chocolate machine on Bratton Fleming station.

The train followed the deep wooded valley of the Yeo, on the up-grade all the way. Through hail and rain the valiant little engine hauled us, past fields, vague and grey and suddenly a brilliant green, everywhere streaming with water. Then an excitement: it stopped. The driver and fireman alighted and walked forward. Heads peered out of windows. The driver returned with a lamb under his arm. Margy purred with sympathy. The lamb was put over the wire fence, to join its frantic ewe.

'Why didn't we use the cow-catcher?' grumbled Windles. 'Instead of stopping the train?'

'You croo' little boy, you!' cried Margaret, adding, with a quick glance at me: 'It's my birthday party, not yours!'

Just before slowing up for Lynton the rain began to fall heavily and we were glad of our raincoats, brought reluctantly by the children and bundled on the wooden rack over our heads.

We walked down the steep stony track to Lynmouth and after some ginger-beer at an inn at the foot of Sinai Hill, we ate our sandwiches in the shelter of a baker's porch, while the rain lashed down. After a three hours' exploration of the beach in the rain, we took the funicular carriage up the cliff to Lynton and climbed to the station again. The railway company had given me a free pass, and so on the return journey I got into the first-class coach, a luxurious pullman made almost entirely of glass, with dark blue upholstery.

'A proper toff is our father,' remarked Windles. From their carriage came shouts, hoots, whistles, and exhortations to the driver. 'Make her spark!'

We changed about at every halt on the line. So did the children, gleefully trespassing into what John called the Vust Class. For ninety minutes they kept up their racket. What vitality!

There were some protests against this miniature railway line being closed. Indeed, Lynton Urban District Council sent a delegation to the Southern Railway Company, with a petition to be presented to the management, who had travelled specially from London to Barum to receive it. The management waited at the town station, on the platform, to receive the delegation from the Urban District Council. But when the train came in, it was empty. Every member of the delegation, to save time, had come to Barum by motor car.

So it was good-bye to the little railway.

That summer was a brilliant season, with much heat. One morning I took my two-ounce rod from its stand in the hall, and went trouting in the river. The air was oppressive. Fishermen had told me that trout were most susceptible to atmospheric pressure; it sent them, dull, to the bottom of the river. I thought I would test this for myself.

Over Exmoor thunder was rolling. I felt the pressure on my head, on all my body. The river shone with a white greyness that hurt the eyes. The green of pasture and oak leaves had an extraordinary stillness. The valley light was underwater light.

Nothing was happening in air or earth or water. Life was static, stagnant. The thunder heat lifted in bourdons of sound that travelled leagues, and returned to meet new shocks from the skies.

I was part of the static, stagnant valley life. I stood at

the edge of the run, at the edge of the fast water running into the pool.

My split-cane rod lay on the grass. The fly-box was open in my hand. There was no energy to select another fly. Nor was there reason: nothing stirred.

For half an hour I had been moving upstream, throwing a hackled fly into all likely places. Not a rise anywhere.

Whiter and whiter the river gleamed, as though it were oil moving there. The eyes were hurt by it. The sky was a vast slate quarry.

Even the horse-flies, which during the past two days of sub-tropical heat had risen in thousands, were gone. Heavy-winged and burring, they had flown to rest on alder leaf and bramble. All life seemed in suspense.

I was wrong; there was movement somewhere. I heard a cry.

A quarter of a mile up river two small figures were running on the bank. The children were bathing under the slight summer waterfall.

Rod in hand, I walked slowly upstream.

It was now greenly dark. Violet flashes ran down the clouds above the lower slopes of the moor. A pheasant grated wildly in the tenebrous spruce plantations on the hillside.

A young sheepdog appeared along the cart-track through the park, fleeing silent and fast, pursued by something we could not see.

Margy, deep brown of leg and arm, and pale of body, skipped about in and out of the shallow water with John, whose fair slight body was ripe barley hue.

The boy picked up an old brass candlestick lying on the gravel and held it high, laughing gleefully at the idea of a candlestick in the water.

Suddenly that candlestick appeared to be alight; the air crackled; colossal noise fell greyly; the figures were blurred. Everywhere glassy toadstools grew on the river.

Cries of terror came from the children.

'Us be getting wet!'

'O, O where be my clothes!'

'Far away in the house! Not even a mackintosh between you!'

'O, O!' More cries of despair and misery.

'Quick, *quick*, Daddy. Can't you see we are getting wet?'

'But you're wet already!'

'Quick, oh! oh! It's raining.'

No argument or exhortation consoled them.

'What's the difference between one wet and another? Aren't the large raindrops quite warm, much warmer than the river?'

No use. It was raining, they had no mackintoshes, they would be soaked. Margy sobbed. John gibbered with rage because I would not share their plaint, but laughed.

While John was crying, I threw off coat and trousers, and splashed into the river. It was a strange feeling, swimming with multitudinous pillars of water arising level with one's eyes, millions of ice-flowers growing instantly and blossoming with white water-drops spilling. It was a delightful feeling, sheltering from the rain in the river.

'Come in, children, it's fine fun!'

'Gitoom, you darned old vool, you!' cried John. 'Us be wet through to the skin, CAN'T YOU SEE?'

7

The Beacon on Ox's Cross

It was the time of King George V's Jubilee, and at night bonfires were to burn on all the high hills of Britain. What finer place whence to see those in our part of the West Country, than from our field overlooking the Atlantic to the west, and southwards hundreds of miles of valleys and ridges of Devon and Cornwall? And why should we not have our own beacon? There was a heap of hedge-parings in one corner of the field, and another heap of brambles left from the winter. Also we had a pile of oak boughs, like an Indian wigwam, for firing, and some of these might be spared. And weren't there some fireworks left over, in the biscuit box? John and Margy had raided the box several times, and despite my threats there had been bangs and shouts outside in the lane. There was one rocket left and some Catherine-wheels.

In the hamlet of Stag's Head they had races on Jubilee Day, followed by a tea in the Village Institute as the village hall is for some reason called. When I had asked Windles earlier in the day if he was going to run, he had shaken his head and muttered that he was no good at running, and then had sprinted away from me at great speed.

John, aged six, explained: 'You see, Daddy, there be

Jan Fry, who's got master long legs and he can run ever so fast, so bestways Windles hadn't better run too, had he?'

'But doesn't he want the money to be given away as prizes, John?'

'Oh yes, Windles wants the money, but he doesn't want to have to run for it.'

'Well, then,' I said to Margaret, 'why don't you run?'

'But if I do,' she said, 'who will look after Topsy?'

Topsy was a little black doll that I had brought home from Georgia for myself a year before; but lately, hearing that Margaret had no doll and was somewhat sad about it, I had given Topsy to her.

They went to the Jubilee tea, and carried home their Jubilee mugs. They were lucky to have those mugs intact; for other children's mugs, a whole boxful of them, had been thrown into the stream beside the village hall, and shattered—some local youth's idea of a joke: so much for the unnatural educational system, I thought.

Now for our expedition to the hilltop field. Having seen that the flags were tied securely to the trailer, that the wireless set was fixed firm between the bundles of blankets, the vacuum water-jug from Florida was full, the basket of food and the box of fireworks on board, the children—less Robbie, who had to be left at home, as being too small—were urged into the back of the open car, to snuggle down in a row with the tonneau-cover up to their chins.

The trailer rattled down the road, behind the car. Flags fluttered on it. The sun shone, the sky was blue. But supposing the portable set in the trailer was being shaken about. Half a mile from home we stopped to see if it were broken, for we did not wish to miss King George V's speech. Windles hopped over the back of the car and switched it on. It broke into song, and was switched off; and we went on for another half-mile before stopping to see if it was still unbroken. After two more stops John, who hitherto had been mute and still with excitement, suddenly announced that if it were left switched on we should then know as soon as it was broken, for then the music would stop. So we continued, the radio click-clacking loudly as it broadcast the noises of the engine's sparking plugs.

We went down the long hill to Swimbridge, through a line of flags over the street, up another hill, and down a farther hill into Landkey village. The children cried out and waved their arms as we went under more strings of flags, the radio pitter-pattered, the trailer rattled, the sun shone. Up another hill, treading on the gas as we left the thirty-mile limit behind and 'Stop, stop!' cried John. 'One of the flags has dropped off!'

'Hurray, let it go!' We went on faster.

'Oh look! The other one's gone,' shouted Windles.

'All the better. We'll get some more in the town.'

'But won't the shops be shut?' suggested Loetitia.

'You must grab a string of flags as we go by,' I shouted to Windles, for a joke.

'Okay,' he shouted back, dubiously.

'P'liceman will have you,' said Margaret.

'Shut up,' said Windles. 'My father can wrestle any policeman.'

'Isn't it all decorated up nice?' said Margaret ecstatically, standing up on her seat.

'Sit down, you little fool,' grated Windles.

'What is the difference between decorated up and decorated down?' I asked Margaret.

'I won't tell,' she grinned.

Loetitia said in my ear: 'Windles is worried, he thinks you meant him to grab some flags.' The flags in the High Street were at least twenty feet above our heads.

'I wasn't serious about the flags, Win.'

'All right, Dad.'

We stopped by the airport beside the estuary and watched a pupil in the dual-control Moth practising landings. While we waited there the squire came up and spoke to us and said he had a beacon on Heanton hill and at ten o'clock was going to send up a five-bob rocket as a signal to light the beacon.

'A five-bob rocket!' said Margaret as we went on.

'That must be a huge one, mustn't it?' said John.

'Gerr't! Branton's got twenty rockets, each costing a pound,' said Windles. 'How much did ours cost, Dad?'

'One penny.'

This information was bound to cause disillusion about our firework-financial status, so I hastened to add that we had also some twopenny Catherine-wheels, and one old Vérey-light cartridge, the last of many raided from the quartermaster's stores on Armistice night, 1918. 'I bagged a pistol also, but honesty compelled me, as soon as I knew the adjutant knew who had got it, to return it.' But this bit of autobiography was of no interest to the children.

'Are we going to have our own bonfire?' asked Margaret.

'Course we are!' growled Windles.

We climbed up St. Brannock's hill, then up the steeper Noman's hill, and along the high ground with its views across an azure sea to Hartland Point and the long grey isle of Lundy floating on the mists dissolving the Atlantic horizon. Coming to Ham village, we saw the Norman church tower, with its gilt weathercock and flagpole flying the cross of St. George, and swifts whistling as they swerved and dived around the lichened stones; and passing on, we climbed the winding lane to Windwhistle Cross and our field.

Now this field was a very special place, to which the family came as a privilege. It was my hide-out, a private place of escape from the world, which included children and other domestic interferences with writing. At least, that was the idea; but in practice all were welcome, and the more (sometimes) the merrier. The field was on a hill-top rising to nearly six hundred feet above the sea. On the map it was called Oxford Cross. There was no river on top of the hill, and no ford that I could see at the four-cross way, once the meeting place of oxen tracks when the hill was downland. In that country an acid soil was grown with heather, ling, bracken, and furze. Rough grazing, in fact.

In days not so long ago, before the invention of cattle floats and the petrol engine, bullocks were driven to Barnstaple market on the hoof. At the cross-ways a piece of the down had been enclosed within stone-and-earth banks, for a cattle park, to use the old word. Here cattle might rest for a night, after being rounded up for the eight-mile walk to market the following dawn. Two acres had been enclosed, and this particular piece of accommodation land (as such splatts or parcels later came to be called in auctioneers' notices) was known variously as Down Close and Ox's Park.

When first I knew it, the four-cross way was a place of romantic loneliness. There was a plantation of mixed pine and beech near the crest, and day after day I walked from the village up the narrow winding lane, sunken six feet below the hedges, to the plantation on the crest, to watch a pair of kestrels which had a nest in one of the firs. Crows and magpies lived there, too, and green woodpeckers came up from the valley to the east, to gouge out grubs boring into the wind-swept trees. There were also ant-nests, beside one of which I found my first woodpecker casting—a pure white cylinder which when broken up disclosed hundreds of little black skeletons.

No sound of foot or wheel ever disturbed the calm spring days. I was alone above a world whose circumambient hollows below were filled by heat-mists, through which gleamed an underlying sea. Cuckoos flew to the trees, gabbling among the leaves as though angry. With excitement I heard the thin reeling of grasshopper warblers in the bramble clumps, and the *churr-churr* of whitethroats. This was in the second half of May, the year was 1914, and I was having my first holiday alone, and in what to me was an entirely new world. Walking ten and fifteen miles every day, I could not have enough of cliff, valley, and hill in this wild and remote north Devon, where the only motor car occasionally to be seen was a grey Mercedes owned by the rector's brother, as it raised clouds of iron-stone dust which had already given a faint tinge of pink to the lime-washed cottage walls of the village which from the high down in early morning was invisible except for a church tower rising among elms.

In the sunshine of the hill I heard a strange tapping. It continued for perhaps half a minute, and was followed by silence. Then it began again. Tiptoeing down the red lane which led to the eastern valley, I came to a bend where an old man was sitting on a heap of stones. He wore a broken bowler hat almost ruddle-red like his face and arms and ragged jacket, and there were eye-shields of black wire gauze over his eyes. He sat upright, his legs forked before him as he tapped with a small-headed hammer on a long and slender handle, splitting stones into a size between walnut and sheep's-nose apple.

I saw him sitting there morning after morning, while the cuckoo called through the haze brimming the valleys below, and the crows and magpies in Windwhistle Spinney, as I had named it to myself, slunk to and fro silently, for their nestlings were fledged. Yet sometimes as I lay quietly in the long grasses of the little field in front of the spinney I would hear a sudden harsh croaking, coming from the air with the petulant cries of a kestrel whose eggs were not yet hatched in a magpie's old nest. The crows were harrying her nest and she was calling to her mate for help. He flew in, to be pursued by the black villains; and this went on at intervals during the day whenever he failed to slip in unseen, with mouse or small bird in his talons to feed her.

The stonecracker was about seventy years old when first I came upon him. Later, after the war, I came to know his son and grandson (who was about my age), a family of stonecrackers. But when the steam-roller and water-cart gave way to the flaming tarmac machine, with lorries bringing a smaller and harder grey stone from the quarries at Brayford, higher up the river where I lived, I saw no more red heaps of ironstone. By this time, too, all the pines in the spinney were dead and fallen, and the beeches were dying.

But to how the name Ox's Cross became corrupted to Oxford Cross: one day in 1907 a surveyor came out from the town and asked Miles, the bearded stonecracker, tapping away on his heap, what the cross-ways was called; and on being told something which might have sounded like *harxencraws us callzn*, wrote down *Oxford Cross*; and Oxford Cross it is called today, although never a neat's-foot waded any river on a hill in Devon.

What was good enough for the Miles family of stone-crackers was good enough for me when, with £100 Hawthornden prize money in 1928, Ox's Cross became mine. And there, in the summer grass, Loetitia came with Windles, then two and a half, and baby John, to see the butterflies and the larks.

Away to the south rose the dim blue tors of Dartmoor, while eastwards rose the curves of Exmoor, lilac in the air of early evening. Gazing to the south again, west of Dartmoor, we could see Brown Willy and his hill-fellows far away in Cornwall.

Sometimes, when the children were in the care of Gwennie, the young maid who looked after them, Loetitia and I went to the field, and making a fire, boiled a kettle for tea. Once we made a map of our new possessions, using ball of string, pegs, and prismatic compass to measure and take bearings; and again, at night, to make a star-map, as in *Bevis*, Jefferies' wonderful story of boyhood. We also marked out corners where trees must be planted, for wind-shields; for one day, we said, we must build a house there, and behind tall palisade gates, and enclosed by trees, we would live a natural life with the children, and forget the world outside, with its cramping ideas and ways.

But somehow, as time went on, life did not turn out as had been imagined; the simple life became complicated, as would-be simple lives do, with the years. However, I had the field; and after the planting of trees, I set about the building of a hut, where I could retire from domesticity, and write. Two men of my own age from the village came to help.

While a rectangular concrete sill was being formed, fifteen feet long and ten feet wide, the village carpenter, Joby, built for me an oak frame in the shape of a small early Saxon church. This frame was assembled in the yard of the King's Arms; after which the holding wooden pegs, which had not been driven home, were tapped out, and the dissembled parts, weighing a ton or more, were carted up to the field. There the foundation plates were bolted to the concrete base. In those days May was usually a fine month in Devon. When erected, the oak frame was a fine sight against the azure sky, where buzzards wheeled and played in the thermals, their wild whistles coming down to where we three were working. I was lodging at the King's Arms, and daily went to Barnstaple to visit Loetitia, sitting up in bed happy with her baby daughter Margaret in a cot beside her.

The trouble with the frame, which had hipped gables, was that it swayed on its bolts, firm set as they were in the concrete. However, across one corner an open hearth was to be built, and when this arose, with a wide shelf of old bricks spread chest-high, and a square chimney-breast rising off the shelf and through the roof peak, the oak frame looked substantial enough to stand through the centuries.

Inside, the chimney-breast was of old red brick; above, the roof the chimney was of local stone, and when finished the hut looked like a miniature church. The 'tower' was surmounted by a weathervane crossed by rods bearing the letters N, S, E, W; and above them a copper fox to swee i' th' wind.

I loved my fox, cut from a cardboard template outlined from another fox above a friend's stables. It was the Fifth Army sign, but without the mud-balled brush of that historic device. My fleeing fox was made by a coppersmith in Bideford, who also made me a kettle, and a lamp to hold half a gallon of oil, for the hut.

Now for shuttering the frame. The upright posts had been sawn, at the mills, with two-inch rebates to take panels of compressed straw which I had imported from France, after seeing them at an Ideal Homes Exhibition in London. When all panels were in position, held by long brass screws, the hut looked to be made almost entirely of straw.

Alas, that I had not thought to cover those panels with bitumen, before putting on the roof of Cornish peggle slates, and the sides of wavy-edge elm boards! But all experience has to be paid for; and I made a further mistake with the roof. The slates were what was called seconds, that is, not of first quality on account of their varying thicknesses. I saved £2 by having seconds, but had to pay an extra £15 in labour to put them on. Each had to be bored with two holes by hand, to take long copper nails by which alone they were held to the roof panels.

As for the panels themselves, within three years those on the west side were rotting behind their elm-board covering, since the wood held the driving Atlantic rains of autumn and winter. But a greater fault lay in the design of the windows. Like many another young man who had had a little success in an imaginative sphere, I did not realize my limitations. So I had insisted that the hut be built my way, with, among other original ideas, windows to open inwards.

If I wanted my own way, so did the elements, particularly the rain! My windows were water-traps. Rivulets streaming down the outsides of the panes during a gale ran between wooden frame and sill, and thence down the inside walls. As for the high winds from the sea, they blew drops from the west window across to the east window; and when I sat at my table writing I was under a continuous shower.

It was certainly the very place for one who boasted a love of the elements and scorned the comforts of ordinary people, and yet where could one find a better dug-out in which to write (one day) my novels about Phillip Maddison's adventures with the Fifth Army in Flanders and Picardy during the Great War? Sometimes as I sat before my fire of driftwood, I might have been in a troop transport upon the sea. Hail rattled on roof and window, draughts moaned through the cracks in the oak floor. The planks were old, and hand-sawn, and fitted imperfectly. They had come from Eggesford House a few miles away, from an old home of the Earls of Portsmouth, which for many years had been derelict to the elements, with all its furniture. Then the fabric of the house had been sold, together with its thousands of squares* of oak flooring, and scores of tons of lead on its roof; and part of the flooring had come to me, beautiful wood, but not exactly tight fitting. So the winter winds whistled up my legs, sometimes almost with the noises of a mad mouth organ. Once, when storm cones were hoisted on the lighthouses of Hartland, Lundy, and Bull Point, a corn sack, laid as a rug before the hearth, rose up as though levitated by an unseen spirit, and began to cross the floor.

* A square in the timber trade is 100 square feet.

In due course I tackled those defects of amateur design. When Loetitia was in the nursing home with her fifth baby I took Windles, then nine, to live with me in the field. The trees were then tall as myself, and the nesting places of various birds . . . but I must tell of that later, for voices outside are crying, 'When are we going to build the bonfire?' The heaps of brambles and blackthorn branches, cut during the winter, must be loaded on the trailer, and drawn to the bonfire site.

The sun was setting, seagulls were flying over slowly towards the sea, and their roosting places on the headland cliffs when our beacon was made. It was eight feet high and held in place by a taller pyramid of oak poles. From the workshop loft, another oak-framed building at the top of the field, came the smell of frying bacon. Up we climbed. I set a bottle of champagne on the table. The bottle had been in the hut for years, lying on its side in the corner of the floor, for just such an occasion as this. Soon we were arranged on odd boxes around the table. Seven candles flickered on the slab of oak used as candlestick—one for each member of the family. The slab looked like a frozen ship, so thick was the wood from past candle gutterings. Windles switched on the radio. Soon the voice of the King, grave and slow, was speaking to us from the air. He sounded exhausted. He had been ill with pleurisy. I could not help my eyes filling with tears; I remembered him in France, in 1914. Nothing seemed to have happened in the world since that time—and now he was old and tired. The years had passed—and I had not yet started the work of my life, which was to re-create a vanished world. Voices were alien about me.

'Cor, I want some champagne,' said Windles.

'I don't. I want ginger-beer,' said John.

'I don't like ginger-beer. I want lemonade,' said Margaret.

'I'm afraid there's only milk,' said Loetitia, sipping a cup of tea, which she preferred to any other drink.

The tarnished gold-foiled bottle glinting in the candlelight was a problem. If it were opened, I should have to finish it alone, and all that wine might make me ill, as I knew from experience. Also, it was not much fun drinking alone. And I was not yet tired or disillusioned enough to drink with ghosts; my life did not yet entirely flow away on the stream of reverie.

'Tea,' said the voice of Loetitia.

Windles was watching me, anxiously. I struggled with a personal or little-ego wish to go away and sorrow alone, in the stream of reverie; but assuming the role of father, replied with assumed cheerfulness, 'Tea goes best with eggs and bacon, I think,' and Windles cried, 'Tea for me, too.' And very good it was, deep draughts from the tall blue pint mug from the Branton pottery.

We were eating bread and marmalade when John said, 'Look, there's something on fire down there!' and going to the window we saw a tiny red glow far away in the dimmit-light. The evening star was shining over Lundy, and the lighthouse of Harty Point was gleaming white, to die away as we watched.

'Why, it's not ten o'clock yet. Someone's fired a beacon before time. It must be boys!'

'P'liceman will get them,' said Margaret, sententiously.

'My watch may be slow.' Leaning out of the window, I saw another speck to the east, in the direction of Dunkery Beacon.

'No, I'm sure it can't be ten o'clock yet,' said Loetitia, 'but perhaps it would be as well if we all went out into the field.'

'Damn, my watch has stopped!'

'Quick, quick!' said Windles, as we got down the ladder.

'Plenty of time, rocket goes up first. Stand back, every one! We don't want it to go into any one's eye!'

'Stand back!' cried Windles, urgently. 'John, stand back, damn you!'

'I am,' murmured John, remaining still.

The biscuit box, containing the few fireworks, stood on the bank near our beacon. I opened it. It was full of biscuits.

'Oh dear,' said Loetitia. 'How silly of me. I gave you the wrong box. I'll go——'

'Certainly not, it doesn't matter. I'll go.'

'Biscuits. Cor, I'd like some,' remarked John.

'John, don't be a fool,' hissed Windles with terrible earnestness. 'We want the rocket!'

'All right,' I said, 'stay there,' and ran to the hut, to return with the right box.

'Oh look!' cried Margaret. 'All those fires. What be 'm, Mummie?'

'They be the Jubilee bonfires, y'know,' suggested John.

'What be 'm for?' asked Margaret.

'You know, Margy, don't you? I told you,' he said gently.

'Be quiet!' cried Windles. 'Dad's lighting the rocket!'

The penny rocket, fixed in the ground, was touched with a lighted match.

'Stand back!'

A small ferocious hissing, and the rocket remained

stuck in the ground. *Pouff!* Its pennyworth of fire had gone.

'But it didn't go up!' cried John. 'Ha ha ha!'

'Our rockets are dud,' I said, putting a match to a clump of furze under the base of the beacon. 'They see our rockets in Australia.'

'Do they really, Dad?' said Windles.

Flame ran up beside one of the oak poles and the wind pressed it to bright anger and soon we were standing in what seemed a great heat and light. Moving to one side we saw in the darkness below many flames extending away to red specks in Cornwall.

There was a strontium glare around Noman's Hill beacon two miles away. Then from Branton, hidden under invisible hills, rockets moved up almost leisurely in thin lines of light, and drooped, and broke into falling showers of colours. 'I can count twenty-seven beacons,' announced Windles when the last rocket's light was fallen. 'I can count only twenty-six,' said John.

'Well, have you counted ours, John?'

'Ooh, no.'

'I counted ours a long, long time ago, while Daddy was piling it up,' announced Margaret.

An hour later our beacon was sunk to embers and only thirteen red spots could be seen from the hut window as the children stood there before climbing up to their blanket beds spread on sacks and coconut matting upon the loft floor.

'Ours was only a little tiny bonfire, not much good,' said John, repeating what he had heard me say only an hour before.

'Well, you look and see,' I said. 'I think it's the biggest.'

A moment before going to the hut to bid them good

night I had thrown the brand ends into the embers and these had now broken into flame.

'Look, ours be the biggest,' said Margaret. 'Ban't it, Dad?'

'Those little tiny ones down there ban't no good,' said John.

'Ah, but they would be if you were near 'em, wouldn't they, Dad? Besides, ours was a very nice little bonfire, I thought,' said Windles.

'Daddy was very clever to make it so quickly, wasn't he?' said Margaret, her mother's imitator.

'People could see it all the way to London I expect,' said John.

Windles caught my eye and laughed.

'My doll hasn't had her supper,' complained Margaret suddenly. 'Nor has her had any tea,' in a mournful voice.

'Ha ha ha!' laughed Windles, finding the remark extremely funny. The children went to bed.

'Will it be Jubilee Day to-morrow?' asked Margaret, hidden under blankets except for eyes and hair. Windles and John exploded with mirth.

'Oh, we are going down to the sea-sands, aren't we, and I shall paddle with my spade and bucket and so will you and so will Topsy, won't she, Mummie?' said Margaret, to change the subject.

'Yes, dear. Now go to sleep all of you. To-morrow we are going to have such a lovely day.'

John was giggling with Windles. 'Oh, such a lovely day,' he mimicked and Windles hid his face under the blankets, whence muffled noises came.

When August came and Loetitia went into the nursing home to prepare for the coming of Williamson *quintus*, I took Windles, as I have mentioned, to live with me in the hut while I worked on its reconstruction. The elm boards were to be removed, to expose the panels of compressed straw, for replacement where rotted, after which they were to be entirely covered by several layers of bitumen.

A year or two previously, while Loetitia and I had been in the United States, hundreds of rats had gnawn a way through the oak floor, to live there during the winter. Mice also had made nests within the mattress of my bed on the shelf above. I didn't mind the mice so much; but the rats were entirely unwelcome. They had gone for the moment; it was September, they were still in their summer quarters within the banks dividing the fields; but soon they would be looking for warmer, drier places.

It was a fine month, and soon I was enjoying the work. Fortunately I had some spare panels, and these replaced the rotting ones on the western wall, those the driving rains had penetrated. We cooked our food on the open hearth, boiling vegetables in a cast-iron crock hanging from the chimney bar, and frying herrings, bacon, and eggs in a heavy pan, also of cast-iron. Usually we went down to swim in the sea in the late afternoon—or I to swim and he to splash about, for I had not been able to teach him the breast-stroke. The sun was our only clock. During the golden September days he spent most of his time by the gate, watching the motors passing on the road to Ilfracombe. Already he was turning into an active nature. At first when I had called to him he had come slowly, reluctantly; then I suggested he should come full speed, like a streamlined railway engine. At once he became the Silver Link. I would shout his name; and *Coming!* the faint cry arose from up by the gate hidden by the dark green boughs of a signal pine; and with elbows and fists working like pistons, he would come dashing down the path scythed through the tall umbelliferous plants and wild grasses. It occurred to me that I had never before seen him running. A dozen times during the day he came to my call: to put a stick on the fire, fill the kettle, set out the plates for lunch, bring in the sleeping-bags in the evening, or help himself to chocolate.

While the bitumen was being slopped on the straw, all social activities were of necessity suspended, or rather abandoned.

Bitumen is an element, unlike tar. It has various forms; and the form I used came out of a forty-gallon drum, and was coffee-coloured when poured out. Soon it turned to a thick black liquid; and once on the brush must be applied before it coagulates. As I worked, layers stuck to my hair and my fingers, to my trousers, and my ribs. Every time drops and splashes fell on my hands they thickened the mass already clotting the fingers. Dry grasses became attached to the mass, binding the fingers tighter. My old flannel trousers stuck to the ladder; the ladder stuck to the eaves of the hut; the brush stuck to the pail, and the pail stuck to me.

Furthermore, bitumen is not a medium in which an impatient man should work for long. No modern sculptor should try to re-create the genesis of Man in bitumen. Art is long, but the patience of bitumen is everlasting. If there is anywhere a brave new artist wishing for immortality in bitumen, let him consider his possible fate; let him remember that there are prehistoric canoes still partly in existence upon whose bottoms bitumen remains as when applied two thousand years ago. Tar breaks up into acids and dusts; bitumen endures. The kind of bitumen I was using was anti-human. Every dip of the brush in the pail increased the size of the brush. After an hour or two of application, the brush which had begun as a modest tenpenny distemper brush was almost the size of a Guardsman's bearskin. My hand, which normally is thin, with slender fingers, became a seal's fin, stuck with grasses and straws and cigarette-ends hidden under a score of layers of sticky blackness. It gradually became a monster stub-wing. Once a pail of the stuff slipped and I fell trying to recover it and it shot over me. By then I was past caring, like Caliban.

My son, a detached observer, heard wails similar to his own when he couldn't get a job done, through impatience. Now he was encouraging.

'You'll soon be finished,' he said. 'I've put some hot water on for you to wash with.'

'Thanks. I'm sorry to keep you from our swim, Windles.'

'No hurry, Father.'

'Wouldn't you rather go down to the village and play with the boys there? It must be dull for you watching me.'

'It is anything but dull, Father.'

'I'll soon be done.'

'There's no hurry, Father.'

'I wonder how the new baby is. Mother says he's dark, like Margy.'

'Ah yes, perhaps it's the bitumen,' he murmured, and fled away up the grassy path to the top gate. Eight years old, and growing to equality with me. I was always pleased when he joked about me. He was, in the freedom and ease of the field, growing to a natural speed and confidence. If only it could continue so, when we got back to the valley cottage, where I was soon to begin and continue (I hoped) another book during the days and nights of autumn, winter, and early spring. . . .

John and Margy came up the hill from the village every day. They were staying with a friend who ran a vegetarian guest house. In that most efficient and modern establishment mutton and beef were called bloody corpse —and certainly when I ate the food there, I felt it was much more satisfying than meat.

It was a quaint sight, John and Margy walking up the hill, hand in hand. Margy with large dark eyes half-hidden by shaggy brown hair, vivid and warm; and John thin and gentle, an expression of mild wonder in his eyes, aloof and seldom perturbed.

'Whatever be 'ee doin' of, Dad?' asked Margy. 'You'm all over ever so black, you knaw!'

'Yes, you be like the Tar Baby,' said John, to whom the story of Brer Rabbit had been read by Loetitia.

I decided the work was done. I had intended to slop seven coatings on the panels, and then to remove the slates and cover the roof. Each slate would have to be numbered, for they were uneven and varied in thickness; it was too much to think about. If the wind drove the rain up under them, the next rainless wind would dry them out. If I removed them, to do the job properly would take a month. I had other work to do: so let the roof remain as it was. My interest in building had for the moment gone. I was sick of bitumen.

Watched by the children, I slit my clotted clothes with a knife, then peeled them in strips from my body. While they were burning in the grass with heavy black smoke, the task with paraffin went on.

The smell of paraffin together with its penetration of

the pores, was odious. Having at last dissolved the bitumen, the next step to freedom was to remove the oil. Hot water and abrasive anti-grease soap got rid of most of it. When through weariness I gave up, Margaret organized a scrubbing of my back and arms. She and John fought for the privilege of washing my head, while Windles waited to sluice me with a bucket of cold water. It was a reviving shock, and we had a chase, the three fleeing from Old Tar Baby. It was their turn to be swished with cold well-water. Cries of protest, but soon we were all running round the field. I don't know what the two old ladies thought, as they looked in the open gateway and saw a half-cast aborigine with several days' growth of beard pursuing three small naked children through the long grasses.

8

Winds of Heaven

The stream that ran down our valley began its life among the wild cotton plants in the bogs of Exmoor. Northwards the high ground was the home of winds. *The pettiness of house-life, chairs and tables, chafes me the year through,* wrote Richard Jefferies. One day towards that winter's end, drawn by hope of a new world, the children and I got in the car, and drove to the top of the moor, where it lay open under the sky. For days, for weeks, in winter the wind veering from the north had seemed to quench all desire for life on the earth. On the moor, one could face the elements directly.

Below the ridge, with its old pack-horse track, lay valleys and hills of a thousand square miles, dissolving to the infinity of mist. Somewhere far below we lived. The sun behind clouds threw down shafts of light like the spokes of a wheel. As the cloud moved slowly towards the south-east the sun wanly lit the withered ling and thin dry grasses of the bog. The bells of the ling were bleached white, the stems tough as though dead. In the whortleberry shoots the rising life was checked by the teeth of deer and wild ponies which wandered there when no other life was moving.

As we walked, the wind's direction changed, and I saw the earth changing. I felt the change in myself, which may be the same thing. So did a lark, which arose singing.

A stone wall raised beside the track and bedded with peaty turves lay on our left as we walked. It seemed strange that this moorland, incult for thousands of centuries, should be owned by anything except the wind and the sky. A farmer's eye saw it as rough pasture land for sheep, which had made many tracks through the ling. Deer and ponies had trodden them wider. If there is a path anywhere, animals of all kinds will follow it, as will children and men.

The storms had beaten and twisted the broad yellow blades from the dead tufts of the moor grass and driven them over the rough face of the moor. They were lodged everywhere between the wires and posts of the fence on top of the wall. So neatly and regularly were the grasses laid in bunches that at first it looked as though a child, impelled by some fancy, had gone along and carefully placed them in position. The unseen child was the wind.

We scrambled under the low wire of the rack, or deer fence, on top of the stone wall, and went our way among rushes and grasses slightly less coarse. Now the reason for the building of the wall was plain: it was reclaimed ground. As we walked on we saw the second sign of life, after the lark's song—black peaty earth moving as an invisible mole beneath cleared out its gallery after the landfalls caused by frost. What soil it was, too, crumbling in the hand, a rich spongy blackness! How the tame flowers in our valley garden would push their roots into it! One day I must return with some sacks, and take home this black virgin soil for their—and my—delight.

Before us lay a rounded mound of earth which the

children climbed, to run down again with arms spread for flight. The mound was the burial place of some chieftain in prehistoric times. While they played and laughed, rolling, wrestling, climbing, I lay on my back and let the wind take my life in its flow. For how many centuries had the warrior been resting in his tumulus, about him the winds everlastingly sighing in heather and rushes, while dark nimbus clouds moved in from the Atlantic and dimmed with rain and mist this ancient, ancient land? Did the wild man wish for burial here, to be always nearest the sky? It seemed to me that he was there still, that the happy cries of the children arising so naturally, thoughtlessly, in the freedom of air and sky, were of the same spirit with him.

Sometimes in the New Year a diamond-hard wind, against which a man could test himself, screamed through the trees of our valley. But these were rare. Most of the gales were soft winds, from over the western hills and the Atlantic waves. The winds roared across the deer park, where old leaves were streaming away, and often, higher in the sky, things like larger, blacker leaves twirling and falling about. These were our aerial neighbours of the woods, rooks and jackdaws, birds which loved playing in the boisterous airs far above the earth. The winds from the Atlantic were warm, turbulent, slap-you-on-the-back-old-fellow winds, and the rooks and jackdaws of Shallowford loved to play in them. How easy it was to bring instant enthusiasm into the children's lives!

'I say, Windles and John, Margy too, Robbie, Rosie —here all of you—let's all be rooks, shall we, walking on the grass, looking for our food, and then, when we're no longer hungry, I'll be the master rook, and call you all up to play in the sky! You face the wind, hold wide your arms, which have feathers on them, give a jump, and launch yourself into the air. That's right! Let's all be birds! Come on, outside. Coats on! All right, we'll wait for you, Rosie and Robbie. To keep yourself in the air, you have to scoop the wind past you with your arms, not beating them up and down, but moving them round in a circle, like this. You see, Windles, birds don't really *beat* their wings, they use them as scoops to push the air behind them. Now just for a minute imagine yourself hastening through long reedy grasses as high as your chest, and how you'd use your arms to help you to get through them quickly. You'd find yourself lifting them up, first one, then the other, and with your hands you'd clear the way for your forward movement, pushing the grasses to either side. That's just what a bird does with the air when he's flying. He scoops the air behind him, and then, just before he falls, he scoops more air, and so thrusts himself through it. Air is like water, only ever so much thinner. It doesn't seem like water to you when you walk on the ground during a still day, but if you try and stand up in a fast car, even our old Alvis travelling at, say, seventy miles an hour, you'll feel at once that the air is like water. But I'm boring you.'

'You're not, you old master rook! You're sporty! Isn't he, John?'

'Coo, yes. Come on, Dad!'

'No, I must go and write now, blast it. Don't make a noise near my door, will you? I'll come later.'

'Okay, Dad, we'll be quiet.'

From my window I saw the leaves, streaming under the beeches and the oaks and the lime trees, and high above the wood on the hillside the rooks tumbling about in the sky. But one must write, to earn money for new coats—though each coat, patched and repatched, travelled from Windles to John, and from John to Margaret, and from Margaret to Robert, and from Robert to. . . .

There was another baby in our house now. He was a crawler, called Richard Leopold Calvert. Neither he nor Robert nor Rosemary had been baptized; we had so far had no time to get round to it. . . .

Coats, boots, stockings, knickers, caps, teeth, food, rent, petrol, and above all, independence—a man must write. Only when work is done can there be relaxation, ease, freedom.

Wind blew down the chimney, wind moaned under the door, gusts shook the casement windows and battering-rams shook the walls. I tried to write, I did my best, I have tenacity which overrides patience, I—but this line is all wrong, and should be torn up. It was torn up. The wind was calling. I was struggling, not against indolence as I had thought, but against nature. Out of the writing-room! Whatever were the children doing in a house on such a morning? Where were they?

'A walk, all of you! Caw-caw! Master Rook calling! Caw-caw!'

No response.

Where were the children?

Windles and John were in the far eastern bedroom. They had gone there to play because 'Our Father was writing, be QUIET, everybody!' They were turning the bedroom, and part of the landing, into a scheme for transporting many truck-loads of coal, iron, wood, and other merchandise, to—well, to where were they taking it all? On the floor lay railway lines, with signals, stations, goods-yards, buffers, turntables. A train service was running—watched by three spectators who were forbidden, with frowns and scowls, to trespass near the lines.

These three spectators, however, were determined to play a part in the organization. Robert, his yellow curls bobbing, held a ship in one hand. He wanted to see that ship sailing along the railway lines. He and Rosie weren't allowed to fill the bath and sail the ship there, so he wanted to see it floating in the next best place, which was on the railway lines on the floor of the bedroom. As I watched unseen, Robert gave the ship to Rosie, who went forward, with a quick glance about her, and stuck the ship right on top of the station roof.

'Get away, Rosie, go down to the nursery!' growled Windles.

'Tidden no real gude, there ban't no water yurr, Rosie,' said John, in his soft voice.

'Yes, there be then!' cried Robert, from the corner. 'Tes all water, ban't it, Rausie, my dear?'

'Yes, Robbie, 'tes water, ban't it?' Perhaps they were remembering the sea, by which they had played and sailed the boat during the summer. Those two bigger boys couldn't get the 'twins' away, so for the sake of peace, and also the running of their organization, Windles and John allowed them to stand there, imagining that the floor was the sea in which the boat was sailing on top of a station roof.

The other spectator was a different problem. He, I noticed, had in one hand an old battered omnibus, with but one wheel on it. That slight mechanical difficulty made no difference to Baby Richard's ambitions. Clad almost entirely in an oversized pair of ragged old grey stockings, which dangled from his toes and entirely covered his legs to his fat little belly, Baby Richard was moving around just as he pleased. As soon as John had picked him up and dumped him, with his battered toy, in the far corner, Baby Richard crawled back, a smile of anticipation on his chocolate-smeared face. Baby Richard's ambition was to run a one-wheeled omnibus on the railway lines. Back he came rapidly, moving swiftly on a three-point chassis—left palm, stocking-covered right leg doubled under him, and battered omnibus clasped in hand—he travelled at a really surprising speed.

'Oh hell, he's back again,' cried Windles, in disgust, as with a cheerful sweep of one hand Richard threw the train off the rails and dumped down the battered omnibus in its place.

'Go away, Rikky, there's a good little man,' said John, in a soothing voice, as he put his arms round the fat little bundle and lugged it back to the corner. Baby Richard crowed with delight, thinking it a fine game. Back he flapped and slid, a happy smile on his face.

'Oh, it's no use with all these confounded kids about,' grumbled Windles. 'Robert, will you bring back that buffer-stop!'

'Tes mine,' shouted Robert, as he went out of the door with the stolen buffer-stop in his arms.

'Yes, 'tes Robbie's,' piped Rosie. It was near their morning bedtime, and Robert wanted to take a buffer-stop to bed with him.

'You thief!' yelled Windles.

'So be you!' retorted Robert.

'So be you,' echoed Rosie. And then they saw me.

'Tidden yours,' said Robert, truculently. 'Tes Windles's!' At this point there was a crash and a cry of mortification from the Managing Director of the Shallowford and District Clockwork Railway (Unlimited), for his train, meeting with no buffer-stop, had run off the rails and crashed over the precipice of the landing and was bumping down the stairs.

'Now you've done it,' said John, serenely. 'Robert, you've broken poor Windles's birthday train.'

Something had to be done, quickly, for I knew how keenly Windles loved his train, and took care of it, always putting it away on a shelf where the smaller children could not get it.

'A real railway smash! Runaway train, falling hundreds of feet over a precipice into the chasm below!'

Seeing Windles's doubtful face, I went on, 'Train wreckers! Blew up your lines with dynamite! It will be in all the papers tomorrow!' And added, 'I think the engine fell on the coconut mat below, and isn't injured after all!'

Fortunately it was true; the engine was not injured.

'Let's go for a walk! The Master Rook will show you how the birds fly.' This seemed promising, so the railway lines were left for Loetitia to pick up and put away, while Robert and Rosie went to bed happily with the stolen buffer-stop. Windles, John, Margy and I went out into the deer park.

We went up a high hill and there we met the full force of the warm sea wind. We spread out arms under our coats and ran downhill, pretending we were birds. The wind was so strong that we could really lean forward, pushing ourselves into the solid-seeming gusts, without any fear of falling. Soon their cheeks were red and their eyes were sparkling. Over us in the sky the rooks and jackdaws were tumbling and cawing, whirling up and down and round and about in a wild game of falling with shut wings and shooting up again into the height of the sky. They cawed and cried *Jack jack-ker-jack*, as they let the wind hurl them about. And after a while they drifted away over the moor, and we went home to our cottage, where, just as I had thought, Loetitia had put away the rails and engines and trucks and stations in the box, and Robert beside Rosie was asleep in bed—their hands open where, ever so gently, the stolen buffer-stop had been taken away.

The daffodils were out in the garden, and Baby Richard was out too. He had been tottering about on his legs for about a month, when the Great Gale came upon our valley. Baby Richard went for his first long walk on that day: the day on which thirteen great trees were overthrown in the deer park; when my wireless aerial was ripped from the larch pole, and flung over the thatch; when the weathervane—a copper fox fleeing into the wind with brush full out behind him—was torn from the roof-ridge and whirled clattering on the garden path. That same mighty wind whirled sleet and snow out of the clouds and choked some of the hedges; it blocked all roads on the moor and buried sheep many feet deep in the fields. All England knew that wind, which scattered tiles and slates off houses, whipped away telegraph wires, and drove waves high over the quays of the fishing village by the estuary. As I was writing, huddled in my chair almost on top of the fire, I heard Margaret's voice saying, 'Where's Rikky? Has anyone seen Rikky? Win, have you seen Baby Richard?'

'No, go away,' growled Windles. He was making a pencil drawing of two heavyweight boxers, with immense muscles. The ideal of terrific physical strength had now taken the place of enormous mechanical speed.

' 'Cause I've lost him,' went on Margaret. 'And, you see, I'm supposed to be looking after Baby Richard.'

On the lawn the yew trees were bending far over towards the east. The air was roaring through the valley. As I looked through the casement window, I saw the top of a spruce snap off in the wood on the opposite hillside. I sat down at the table again, abruptly to be smothered by wood-ash and hot air. The pale flame on the hearth of wood-gas was licking across the brick hearth to the beech-wood floor. The chimney thundered.

Every year at Shallowford, at baby-tottering time, the daffodils in the garden beds and lawns, and at the bottom of the hedge were sacrificed to rising human life. Words of protest, shouted or persuasively soft, were unavailing. The flower-heads were bright and enticing; and so they were taken. When at last Baby Richard was found, two hundred yards away in the deer park, where he had wandered alone, he clutched a daffodil in each fist. He was sitting beside a new-uprooted beech tree, while the gale roared around him. And he was happy. Not in the least bit worried by the brutal ice-shocks of wind! He was wearing a suit which once Windles had worn, then John, then Margaret, then Robert. I had bought it six winters before, in New York, after seeing small children in similar clothes running about the streets when the weather was below zero. The hat was like a flying helmet, the trousers and jacket were made of the same stuff, zip-fastened. One of the kids on the sidewalk said the suit was called a windbreaker. And in the bleak, rocky country of the New England seaboard it takes something to break up the force of the wind which rushes down from

Top: *In May of 1925 Henry married Loetitia Hibbert of Lancross. They had met when otter hunting on the nearby Torridge river.* Left: *The first baby, 'Windles', wrapped up in cold March weather at Georgeham. Henry's mother had come from her home in Kent.* Right: *Windles was taken to Barnstaple for his first studio photograph when Henry received the enormous sum – for him – of £100 as prize money for* Tarka.

Top: *The house at Shallowford had small rooms and thick walls and thatch insulated the brood of children from cold Atlantic gales which swept daily into the valley.* Bottom: *The valley of the Bray was warm in summertime. Its wild parkscape became the happy playground of Henry and his children.*

Top: *Windles and John have a tub in the garden, and Windles and John wearing Appledore fishermen's jerseys knitted in the salmon-fishing country twenty miles downstream.* Bottom left: *Henry spent many happy hours building dams to aerate the water for his salmon and trout.* Bottom right: *John and Margaret who became inseparable companions. Henry's bow-tie and moccasins betray a recent visit to the New World.*

Top: *The Humpy Bridge over the Bray. Here was a deep pool for the salmon to rest when they had been fed.* Left: *Windles, Margaret and John by the fireplace of Shallowford, built to Henry's design.* Bottom: *Baby Richard was too small to join Windles, John, Rosemary, Robbie and Margaret for a ride in their uncle's car to South Molton.*

Rosie, John and Robbie in the garden. John always looked after the younger ones, and once saved Robbie from drowning. Below: *John writing his book.* Bottom: *On spread-out Great War army blankets, the children await dusk and the Jubilee beacon.*

Top: *Baby Richard cries, watched benignly by Windles but with indifference by Robbie.* Middle: *Henry and Windles supervise the building of the bank which marked the boundary of the new property at Ox's Cross.* Bottom: *Ox's Cross writing hut nearing completion in the sheltered south-west corner.*

Top: *Watching for leaping salmon on the Torridge river, Henry was preparing to write* Salar the Salmon. Bottom: *Goodbye Shallowford. The author uprooted himself and his family in the late 1930s to take up a new life 300 miles east.*

Top: *John, Windles, Richard, Margaret and Robert at the long oak table for Christmas 1936 at Shallowford.* Bottom: *John, Robert, Margaret, Windles and Richard outside the new house which Henry built but never occupied at Ox's Cross, August 1977, the day of Henry's funeral.*

Labrador. The wind which tore across England on that Sunday was the same kind of wind, tumbling invisible icebergs of air, howling down from the Arctic where polar bears prowled for seals lying on the ice-floes. Lucky for Baby Richard that he wore the maroon-coloured reach-me-down suit of his brothers, with its zip fasteners down trouser-legs and up to his throat! There he sat, beside the uprooted and shattered tree, his legs in short little rubber boots stuck out before him, smiling at the flower-heads he had pulled from their stalks, while all around him was being beaten by a seventy-mile-an-hour gale.

I picked him up and carried him into the house, and Loetitia turned on the bath, for his hands were blue. When he saw the bath Baby Richard uttered a strange noise like that of a squirrel scolding a man who gets too near its young ones in spring: a sort of screech, the more surprising when uttered out of a little round white face, with large solemn brown eyes, which remains simple and silent-looking. The screech was sudden as it was short, not in the least like a baby yelling or even shouting. It could be heard a long way away, like the short blasts on the whistle of a goods train starting in Filleigh station on a still summer day. To make this noise, which was uttered to call attention to something urgent, such as the need for chocolate when Rosemary or Robert was being given a piece, or for Loetitia glimpsed in another room, or for a sight of pictures in a newspaper being read by someone else, or for another spoonful of egg while the preceding spoonful was still in his gullet, or for a too-early bath or bedtime . . . to make this noise, the mite apparently filled himself with air, and expelled it, all at once, in a short sharp grating cry.

The bath was turned on, and seeing it, Rikky uttered his screech. It was not his bathtime. For one thing, his tub mates, Robbie and Rosie, were boxing. That is, having taken Windles's set of Christmas-present gloves, they were dancing around and waving their hands up and down, laughing and shouting.

If Rikky was to have a bath, Rosie and Robbie must have one too, so the gloves were dropped and the two scrambled upstairs. John, playing a game of Patience by himself under the dining-room table, which to him was a cave in the mountains, was sent upstairs to be in charge of them. John thought he could be in charge better if he too got in the bath, so off came his clothes and into the water he went. Each child had its own bit of soap, each its own tooth glass and brush—Robbie and Rosie and Rikky had a potted-meat jar each—and with John to see they didn't break the glasses or come to any harm, they splashed and played. With them in the bath were Rikky's rubber sponge made like a monkey, Robbie's hot-water bottle made like a cat, and Rosie had a candle, which floated, and a sodden box of matches which wouldn't open.

Then Windles and Margaret, attracted by the noises of shouting and laughter, went upstairs to join in the fun. Six of them in the bath all together! Shrieks as Windles emptied a potted-meat glass of cold water down John's back. Yells as John tickled Windles's tummy. Squirrel-like yelps from Richard, of complete happiness: cries of excitement from Robert, words tumbled all together as he began each sentence with the usual, 'I-I-I-I-I'll tell 'ee suthing——'

It was inevitable that amidst such high excitement there should eventually arise yells of protest and even rage; and there were John and Margy fighting over the ownership of an inflated pig. Whereupon the door opened and a voice roared, 'Out of it, all of you, and Windles will mop up the mess and leave the bathroom tidy.'

'Okay,' said the Managing Director of the Shallowford Kids Clockwork Railway, etc., etc., etc.

Afterwards, six children in dressing-gowns in the sitting-room, munching hot toast before a blazing wood fire. Outside the dark yews bended to the howling blast, as though gravely protesting against the violence of the noisy young wind whose life, for all its bluster and power to blow down lesser trees and scatter tiles and slates through England, would last but a few hours. So twilight crept into the valley, while faces glowed in the flames of the hearth, and the littlest ones grew sleepy, and were carried to bed upstairs.

9

Freshet

Again it was the fall of the year. How had it come so quickly? Sometimes we walked beside the river, for it was the season when salmon and sea-trout ran up from the sea to spawn. Leaves swirled away with the brown glissades slipping under the triple falls of the bridge.

One day, traipsing along with the children beside irregular ribbands of moorland reed, feathers, sticks, tins and bottles washed down from villages and hamlets up the valley during the floods, I told the bigger boys what to do if one of the small children were to fall in. The only chance of rescue was to run down-bank in the hope of the drowning child being taken into an eddy where the water either stayed slack, or revolved beside the main stream. It would be useless to try and get the child out by wading into the raging spate.

'Coo, yes,' said Windles, eyeing the white leaping waters below the falls.

'Don't be scared if a child falls in. Use your head. There may be a chance for one of you to grab it out, at an eddy. Let's come downstream to Stag's Head weir, and see if any salmon are jumping. It's time the greenbacks, or early clean-run fish, come into the river. Look, that's what is meant by an eddy. See how the water's pushed backwards by the main flow? You could lean down and get a grip on a kid washed into the deeper water here. It would be your only hope.'

As we climbed over the wooden fence by the road bridge, John said that no salmon would be running. Asked why, he explained that he had seen two herons.

'I zeed ould cranes standing beside the river higher up, at the edge of the smooth water. If the fish had been below the falls, the ould cranes would have been to Stag's Head falls!'

I was delighted with this perception, and said, 'That's a fine bit of natural reasoning. How came you to think of that, John?'

John coloured slightly and said, 'Well, you see, Dad, that's what you told Windles and me last year, and I minded it.'

The river level was dropping fast, the water fining down after the freshet, as the little spates were called in Devon. The rain had not lasted long enough to break the springs after the unusual winter drought.

It took about half an hour to reach the falls. We went along the path through the wood, up and down a rocky place, more adventurous than by the meadow on the opposite bank. At the weir, we stood and gazed at the thundering water. After staring at the white cascades it seemed as though the river above the fall was moving backwards with the landscape. No fish appeared, and we thought we would go and look at the spillway of the mill-stream which fed the water-wheel of the saw-mills. It was Sunday, and no men would be working there.

The water had now dropped back enough for one to walk across the sill of the weir.

Taking off shoes and socks and rolling up trousers I felt my way, foot sliding before foot, across the slippery slabs of stone mortared there. Half-way across, judging it to be safe, I returned for John. The water was only about six inches deep, but it pushed hard against my legs, and made my bones ache. Dumping John on the other side, I returned for Margaret. She whimpered a bit, and clung tensely to me. Meanwhile, Windles had disappeared, so I walked back again and joined the two on the right bank. We went along a path through brambles, and over a narrow plank parallel to the iron door or fender under which the mill-stream boiled and swilled. We were then on the meadow, beside the leat which led to the mill-wheel. The water in the leat was deeper than a man, and about eight feet wide. An ugly place to fall into, when the wheel was working, I told the children.

As the mill-wheel was not working, we crossed the mill-stream again by a narrow bridge made of two planks laid together, and so to an island where heaps of sawdust were dumped among pines and rhododendrons. Down one side of the island the water escaped over a spillway. We sat above it and watched thin white water surging down the sloping stone face below.

We had not been there a minute when a sea-trout appeared out of the white turmoil and began to swim violently up the spillway. The water was shallow, and looked like white fleeces lying on the slope. The upper part of the fish's body was in the air. Half-way up it was exhausted, and lay on its side a moment before being washed down again. As we watched, another smaller fish swam up and rested in a tiny eddy just below the lip of the spillway, where a rusty fragment of scythe-blade was wedged. Slowly it edged itself up to the water-fleece before giving a leap and threshing up in what looked like a series of leaps.

The little spotted mother-of-pearl fish got to within three feet of the top and then clung with its paired fins to the stem of a dock which was growing between the crevice of two stones. The water, almost as thin as a snail's shell, barely washed over it. It rested there nearly a quarter of an hour, its tail curved round the base of the dock. Just above it was a miniature turbulent pool about as big as my two hands, made by the dislodgement of one of the stones. With a sudden spring and rapid flicker the fish was in this pool and lying there with its brown tail out of water.

'Isn't it a darling little fish?' said Margaret.

'Coo, sporty,' said John.

It was past teatime, but the sun was shining, and we wanted to see what the fish would do. 'Look, Margy and John, this fish has come about twenty miles in from the sea, after travelling scores of miles around the coast to find the mouth of the river where it had been born.'

'I hope they ould cranes won't get it,' said John. Hardly had he spoken, when there was a harsh cry of *Krar-k!* in the sky, and looking up, we saw a heron flying over.

'It swore at us, John.'

'Bissley ould bird,' said John.

'I don't like 'n,' said Margaret.

Windles was playing with his train when we returned. 'Darn, I didn't want to be drowned,' he grumbled.

The next day, returning from school, John went alone to the spillway, and there he saw two large square tails, side by side in the turmoil below the little cascade. As he was leaving he saw a heron circling above the tree-tops, so he went back and tapped the tails with a stick. 'Cor, they salmonses didn't half spark!' he told me.

Next Sunday conditions for seeing salmon were better. It rained all the Saturday night, a proper sou'-wester, the wind blowing smoke into the sitting-room. A puff or two of smoke didn't matter, it was aromatic wood-smoke from a back-stick of pine: a burning wood that required watching, since its grain often snapped in flame, and sparks flew into the room. As the rain was lashing down the window panes, and the wind thundering the chimney, we sat before our fire and played games. Windles, now ten years old, played draughts with me, and with two off my side of the board, he usually beat me. Then he played with John, with three off his side, and it was anyone's game. Afterward Robert, who was three, played with John, but before John could win Robert usually got tired of draughts, and started playing wheels with them all over the board, and rolling them about the floor. While he was doing this, Baby Richard would be trying to climb up my trousers to see if there was anything eatable on the table.

But next morning the sun shone through the clouds. 'Why does Mummy never come for walks with us?' asked Margy.

'Let's ask her,' I said. 'She hasn't come for a walk with us for years.'

Loetitia was always working; from before seven in the morning until after ten at night. We asked her now, but she said she had the Sunday dinner to cook, and the little ones to look after. 'Don't worry about me, enjoy yourselves,' she said. So the three children and I set out together. The boys had on their Wellington boots and mackintoshes, and carried sticks. We should need the sticks for going along the slippery rock path at the bottom of the valley-side wood, which wound up and down, sometimes very steep and narrow, among the trees.

To get to the wood we had to cross a small meadow. There two moorhens were squatting in the hedge. They flew away at once, back to the river. 'I expect they're a bit cold,' remarked Windles, 'and sitting up there to keep as dry as possible.'

John thought a moment before replying, 'But they be waterbirds, like ducks, ban't 'm, and they shouldn't mind a bit of wet, I should think.'

'Perhaps they are up there to keep out of the way of otters.' I told them how once I had found a rabbit crouching in the grass, badly hurt by an otter, which had mauled it and then apparently let it go again. 'Otters usually live on fish, which they hunt underwater and eat on the banks; but when the river is in spate, they find it hard to catch fish, and hunt the runners, ditches, and rabbit warrens.'

Today the path through the wood was hidden by leaves blown down in the gale. Branches of fir trees lay there too. We picked our way, taking care over patches of rock which showed along the path.

At length we came to the steeply rising part, where a slip would mean a fall into the swollen river below. Rubber Wellington boots were liable to slip on rock, and so I climbed down and stood at the edge of the river, while the climbers picked their way upwards.

The river was brown-coloured and running as fast as a trotting horse: but it was fining down: most of the washed-out soil from the field-drains and ditches had been left in the eddies, or gone out to the distant estuary. The falls were about a quarter of a mile below, and we could already hear the noise of the tumbling waters.

As we came nearer the weir, the dull growling echoing back from the trees became a roar. A mist of spray hung about the trees there. The water bended over the weir-sill smoothly before gashing itself white and plunging on the rocks below. Half a tree, uprooted and washed down by the greater spate of the night before, was lodged on the rocks. We stood on the bank below the weir, in the misty roar, and suddenly we started back, for from just below our feet a big grey bird flew up, and flapped desperately away over the weir. 'Darned ould crane!' cried Windles and John together, and burst out laughing, for they too had been startled. For an instant it looked as though the heron's wings might strike the branches of the uprooted tree, but it just cleared them. It was nearly five feet across the wings, with a long thin neck and sharp yellow beak, and legs hanging like stilts. It had been standing on a ledge of rock below, waiting to spear any trout that should come within striking distance. There were many trout, both silver sea-trout (locally called peal) and brown river-trout, trying to jump over the weir, and the heron was amusing itself lancing them. One large female fish lay there, picked open, for the rows of berry-like eggs within.

We had not been waiting more than a minute when we saw a fish about a yard long leap out of the white water and fall half-way up the face of the weir. As it struck the water again it swam vigorously, and we could see it hanging there, as though trembling violently. It clung there for about ten seconds, holding by its paired fins, and then it gave up, and was washed backwards, turning upside down in the boiling white water, and away in the surge of white waves. The water was too strong for so big a fish.

Almost immediately afterwards another salmon leapt about two yards from where we were standing. It fell on a hidden branch of the tree, and clung there. We could see the water pounding its body. Then with a half-spring and desperate wriggle it was two feet higher up, swimming with all its strength, gradually moving upwards. But the fall of water was too heavy, and it was swept backwards. We saw the spots on its red flank and yellow head as it turned over. It was a cock-fish, a 'soldier'. At spawning-time some of the cocks turned almost as red as a brick, and their heads went as yellow as a canary. It was the wedding-dress of the new-run fish, come into the river direct from the sea.

The hen-salmon varied in colour from dark bronze to olive-brown. Some of the fish had yellow fungus-patches on fin and scale; these were the fish which had come into the river months before the spawning season, and had languished in the shallow waters of summer without feeding.

We saw several salmon trying to jump the weir, but none got up. Fish do not like such places, I told the children; indeed, they are afraid of them, dreading hurts and bruises like any other animal—furred, scaled, or skinned. But the instinct to spawn is greater than that of comfort; it drives them up the river, to the spawning-beds in the gravel.

There was a fish-pass at the side of the weir, but the wooden door was closed. We tried to lever up the fender with rotten sticks, but it was stuck too tight. So I stood in the water to my waist and heaved it up with my fingers crooked underneath the half-rotten bottom. Then we went back to below the weir, and watched the mud being swept away. Afterwards, when it had cleared, we saw a reddish back-fin and tail-tip sticking out of the water, in the calm patch between the stream and the eddy it formed. I touched it with my stick, and it did not move. Perhaps it was a fish that had hurt itself on the rocks, and was feeling numb along its body. So I climbed down and, putting my arm in the water, pushed it away into safety—for the heron would return when we were gone, and would stab it with its beak. The salmon slowly swam away.

Too soon it was time to think of returning for dinner.

'What a damned nuisance meals are! Let's wait until we see a fish get over the weir!'

'Cor darn, I be hungry, I be!' said John.

'Just one fish.'

We were lucky, for soon afterwards a sea-trout about twelve inches long succeeded where the heavier fish had failed. The small silver fish, with dark spots and clove-shaped marks on its flanks, leapt with superb confidence out of the boiling turbulence, fell on a mossy rock, and after resting a few seconds, started to swim straight up into the solid fall of water. We watched it moving inch by inch upwards, seeming to vibrate within the water, to be drawn upwards slowly on an invisible string; and at the very lip of the water it gave a sort of spring, and was over the bend of the sill and into the pool above. There it gave a leap and fell back with a splash, as though of joy for its success. It seemed a good ending to our visit, and we went home to dinner, only fifty minutes late.

10

John Shows a Cool Head

A few weeks later, in the middle of January, I went away to London. While I was there, something happened that I learned of only when I read *About My Life*, which was the title John gave to the autobiography he was writing. When I questioned Loetitia and John about it, I pieced the facts together, into the following account. I have also got permission from the author of *About My Life* to print his book, or such selections of it as are deemed fit to be published (for one chapter at least was starkly realistic, with ancient Anglo-Saxon words that are not usually printed). In those pages the reader will notice the laconic calm of John's style, compared with my own nervous, multi-detailed prose: contrast between classic and subjective styles.

At the time of the occurrence, that January, Robbie and Rosie were three and a quarter years old, and John was eight. John, the reader will have observed, was a kind child, always ready to help or amuse the younger children. Robbie and Rosie loved being together, and playing together, but they also loved the same toys. Often, therefore, when left alone in the nursery there came from that room screams and swear-words, and looking through the upper glass panels of the door, the beholder would observe two diminutive individuals pulling one another's hair, while hitting, tugging, kicking, and even biting. But when John played with them, Rosie and Robbie loved one another. Rosie had only to go away for a week to stay with her grannie, for Robbie to be most unhappy; and when she returned, cries of delight would accompany the armfuls of his toys held out for Rosie to accept. There was a difference between them that I observed more than once. If Robbie had a bag of sweets, he would offer them all round; if Rosie had a bag, she would hold on to it, if grown-ups were about. Alone with the children, however, Rosie would become more open, less of the screwed-up-tight sort of feeling, and would naturally share with the others. Her grandmother adored her, and, I thought, by lavishment upset the balance of the child's personality; but among children, Rosie became more or less unprecocious. Now for the incident at Sawmills Weir.

Holding in each of his small hands a still smaller hand, John took the 'twins' for a walk. It was a Sunday afternoon, when the saw-mills were idle, and no one about.

'I'll take 'ee to see Daddy's samons, you'll see them jumping about, you will.'

'Yaas, us wull, won't us? See Daddy's samons,' said Robbie to Rosie and Rosie to Robbie.

It was too difficult to go by the woodland path, so John led the two smaller children along the road to the bridge, and then over a keeper's stile into the meadow. They walked through the grass. The river was still high after the rains. The water ran fast, much faster than they could walk. White waves broke over hidden rocks. 'There be lots of samons in there, only you can't see 'm,' said John.

'Yaas, there be lots, ban't 'm, Robbie?'

'Yaas, Rausie, there be lots and *lots*.'

The river swirled deeper under the trees on the opposite bank. It was salmon-running water: sparkling with oxygen. The first flush of dirty road and ditch water had ceased to stain the sea of Bideford Bay by several days.

The trio had to unclasp hands in order to get through a black iron-railing fence, but once through, they joined up again and went on beside the deepening water of the mill-pool. When almost across the second meadow John stopped, just as he remembered Father had once stopped, and said: 'Can you hear the weir roaring? 'Tes the thunder of the falls!'

They listened. Robbie said, 'Yaas, Robbie can hear, Johnnie.'

And Rosie said, 'I can hear too, can't I, Robbie?' She stared at the sky.

'No, that's rookses cawing up there, Rosie, that ban't the thunder of the falls,' said John in his gentle voice.

'Yaas, it be, ban't it?' cried Rosie.

'Come along, Johnnie will show 'ee the weir,' and the three trailed on through the grass.

On the right bank of the river, at the apex made by bank and weir, the water in the deep, stone-faced leat wimpled away under the iron fenders, on its way to the mossy water-wheel. The iron fenders could be worked up or down, to pass a larger or smaller flow to the wheel. When let down, the doors stopped all flow of water. The leat was about a hundred yards long, and as has been said, eight feet wide and six feet deep. When the mill was working, the weight of water falling continually on the troughs of the wheel bore it round, rotating a shaft on which pulleys revolved, turning belts which worked the saws which cut tree-trunks into posts and rails and planks. This wood was used to repair the gates and cottages and fences and farmsteads of his Lordship's estate. But John had learned another aspect of land ownership.

'Tes Cold Pudding who owns all this yurr wood you see,' he said. 'He's a dear little man, if you don't vex him by saying he rides a sheep instead of a hunter. Us'll go quietly now, Rosie and Robbie, and us may see Cold Pudding.'

The great circular saws, which whirl round and cut swiftly into the trunks with rasping, screeching noises, were silent. No timber-wagons, with horses mudded to the knees, stood there; no men heaved at the straight and massive trunks with crowbars, or made piles of new-sawn wood. The sawmills were silent. Trees echoed the roar of the falls, and the lesser thresh and play of water cascading down the spillway of the leat.

Stepping cautiously to the waterside, John peered into the deep, dark water. Was that a salmon down there? Robbie and Rosie peered into the leat. No, it was only a bit of an 'ould tree', declared John.

A thick plank, called in Devon a clammer, crossed the leat, lying almost level with the water. It was on this plank that wheelbarrow-loads of sawdust were taken, and dumped on the little island. Beyond were the loveliest heaps of sawdust! Oh, they must get across, and play with them!

'Be careful,' said John, as all three crossed slowly on the clammer plank. It was scarcely more than a foot wide. The water rippled as they trod on it.

A happy child has no sense of time, and hardly an idea of place. It lives as the air moves. Among the sawdust,

John Shows a Cool Head

John and Robbie and Rosie played, crying one to another to see what each was doing, discovering, pretending. They ran up and down and fell over; they grabbed handfuls and flung them into the air; they chanted 'King of the Castle'. Robbie said, 'I'll t-t-t-tell 'ee Jannie, suthin'! I'll have a sawmill when I be a man, so's I can always play all day with the doust!'

One heap was white, from ash trees sawn for making parts of carts; another was pink, from centuries-old yews. After a while, Robbie said, 'I-I-I-I'll tell 'ee suthin'! Let's pretend us be feeding Daddy's samons!' and ran with two fistfuls to the water's edge. He stood on the plank and cast handfuls into the water. The coloured dust floated. It made patterns as of lace. The current slowly gathered it to the plank at their feet, then slowly sucked it under. Robbie went back for some more. He was enchanted by the way it lay on the water, and stood there alone while John and Rosie played on the top of the pink heap.

'Come yurr, Rausie, midear, 'tes sporty,' he cried, and thought it so nice that he walked on it.

Hearing the splash, John turned round. 'Oh,' he said quietly. He went white in the face. Rosie looked at Johnnie, and seeing his face, began to whimper. 'Robbie's valled in,' said John, as matted curls, covered with sawdust, showed by the plank. Rosie clutched herself and screamed. Her cries echoed back from the sheds of the silent sawmills.

John remembered the whistle with which Daddy called him. So he gave the whistle, hoping that Windles might hear it. But Windles was away by himself somewhere. 'Oh,' said John again, for Robbie was screaming as he struggled under water.

John ran to the plank and caught hold of Robbie's hair with his two hands. Recently Mother had wanted to cut it, for it fell lower than his shoulders; but Daddy always said, 'No, I love to see it, it is beautiful hair, and I want to see it even longer, right down to his waist, in fact.' This always vexed Mother, for she had to comb it out and brush it when Robbie came home after making mud pies by the river. John clutched the long hair, and tried to pull Robbie out. He was not strong enough. The current was trying to drag Robbie under the plank. Rosie saw Robbie's rubber Wellingtons drawn off his feet, and screamed all the more, as she peered into the water. Rosie was short-sighted, and bent down to peer at things.

'Keep away, Rosie,' said John, faintly pink in the face. 'Go on the grass, get away from the water, I tull 'ee!'

But Rosie screamed more and more and clutched herself tighter, all drawn up into a knot of fear. John let go Robbie's hair with one hand, and taking her by the hand, he yelled, 'Stand still there, I tell 'ee, wull 'ee?' He knelt on the plank, straining and tugging to get Robbie out of the water. Oh dear! Robbie was too heavy. He was spluttering and choking. 'Help,' cried John, but only the rooks answered, cawing overhead.

Then he remembered what he had been told he must do if a child fell in the river during a heavy spate; he must run downstream to an eddy, in the hope of catching and pulling out the child where the current was checked or even backward-turning. He must never try and pull a child out against the power of water. So John let go Robbie's hair, watched him carried under the oak clammer plank, and trembling, grabbed the hair again on the other side. Holding on with all his strength, he pulled Robbie to the side, and after a long time, managed to get him out. He staggered with him over the plank, and held his head down while Robbie sicked up a lot of water.

When Robbie was better, but still crying, and Rosie howling, John carried Rosie, stiff and heavy with fear, over the clammer plank. He took each by a hand and led them home. He carried Robbie over the muddy places, for Robbie had only his socks on, and they were half off. At home Mother put Robbie into a hot bath, and soon all was well again. And then John told Robbie a story about a salmon that was wearing his Wellingtons, at the bottom of the river, and Robbie was glad that the fish would keep his feet dry.

Perhaps the most remarkable thing is that the chronicler of the children of Shallowford, who was away in London at the time, it will be remembered, never learned of what happened until he read it, half a year later, in John's book.

Since Michaelmas our Yule log had been propped against the walling of Humpy Bridge. A freshet brought the log down one day, and the boys and I hauled it out with a lasso. It weighed about one and a half hundred-weight, and was of yew.

Many times I had wondered if it were not too good for burning: if that salmon-pink wood, stronger than oak, should not be reserved for table-legs.

A crack running by a twist in the stick finally decided me. There stood the Yule log, which we intended to drag into the sitting-room on Christmas Eve.

The small children were excited, and had been rehearsing in make-belief for days. A minor hitch occurred when Charlie the black cat ate three-year-old Margaret's 'yoolug'—a piece of bacon-rind on a string.

For the holidays walks had been planned—whatever the weather—on the high ground of Exmoor and down the lanes with their tall beechen hedges. A blazing wood fire would greet us when we returned, pleasantly tired, to sip tea made from the black iron kettle hanging on its lapping crook from the chimney bar.

We got a spruce fir, with all its roots; it was set in an oak tub, for later planting-out in the company of its brethren in the field below Windwhistle Spinney.

Late on Christmas Eve, when the children were lying excitedly awake upstairs, or breathing sweetly in sleep, Loetitia hung its branches with shimmering delights. Then into the cupboard under the stairs, until the afternoon party!

Of course every child had hung out a stocking. And of course Father Christmas filled each stocking, and presents were opened while we were all sitting around the long refectory table at breakfast.

Afterwards a two-mile walk across park and fields to church. On the way we peered over the parapet of the bridge to see if any of the spawning salmon were visible. And we saw the anthill beside the river where every travelling otter scratched and rolled, a small hillock very green in spring with the fishbone fragments nourishing the root grasses.

Before the church service everyone greeted everyone else in voices that were neither too loud nor yet too subdued. Contrast is the salt of life; and, after the singing of the good old hymns, we returned to see Riddy sitting beside the turkey turning slowly on the jack-spit by the hearth. And what a fire! The wood for it had been selected and matured for several years. Pine for resinous scents; oak for body; elm for its majestic white ash; alder for charcoal—in fancy the flames of these woods blended and gave flavour to the bird.

Rows of faces perched themselves along the table, Father refused to carve, corks popped with bubble of grape and ginger, then the lighted pudding, set with holly-sprigs, came in with the mince pies, to be eyed with lessening enthusiasm except by the rows of brighter faces. Now for the crackers! And figs, dates, nuts and raisins.

What energy the children had! Ping-pong—skittles—bagatelle—lead-horse-racing—crown and anchor—halma—snakes and ladders: interrupted by the voice of the King, symbol of our hopes, speaking around the earth. He spoke slowly; he had been very ill; but none could doubt his simple goodness.

When the children had returned from a walk, Windles ran in to tell me that he had seen Father Christmas's reindeer. They were going up the path to Bremridge Wood . . . or else they were the red deer from Exmoor, driven down by the hard weather. Which were they, Dad?

'Quick, Windles, tell the others what you've seen! What luck, to see the real Christmas deer!'

II

Threshing

After the rains of January, sunshine and clear skies, mellowing to hues of sunset; the evening star shining whitely in the twilight; and with open starry nights, the frost. White hoar covered the lawn and the flower-beds below the bedroom windows, though the sun was shining above the valley. The dark of the year was turned, and a man might look forward to the spring and summer. The cottage lay at the bottom of the valley, and the trees growing on the slopes in front of us stopped the sunshine in the lower rooms for six weeks in winter. With the sunlight in the breakfast-room, hope came again.

One morning when I looked out of my bedroom window, the keen frosty air was exhilarating. It was going to be another still, golden day. Sunshine is life—sunshine is laughter—certainly I heard laughter. Other sounds, too, thumping noises, and a shout in a high, excited voice—John's voice. The thumping noises increased until they ended in a bang and much laughter in which could be heard the loud ha-ha-ha-has of Windles. The pouting, indecisive Windles seldom returned after those summer weeks in the hut, when we put the bitumen on. He was no longer ashamed of his body, or of me. He laughed with loud glee. Something too good to be missed was going on. I went along to their bedroom.

A fight was in progress. But not the kind of fight another man wants to join in, either with fists or angry tongue. This fight was a game. Both John and Windles had thrown off their pyjama coats and wore only their trousers. John's trousers were about to slip down. This was a peculiarity of John's trousers. They were fitted with the usual cord or string about the middle; but this never appeared to be fastened. So whenever I saw John in pyjamas, he was invariably supporting his trousers with his left hand. Again and again he hitched them up; but never appeared to have learnt that a bow-knot would have done the work for him.

For Christmas they had received a pair of boxing gloves, which they had coveted ever since listening on the wireless to the fight between Walter Neusel and Ben Foord. Afterwards I had observed Windles to be hitting sundry cushions about the house. He punched coats hanging on their pegs in the hall. He delivered, on the back of my padded leather armchair, short-arm jabs and round-arm swings. He upper-cut rows of washing on the line; he knocked-out toy balloons and once, Baby Richard's bedding airing on the pram. Robbie copied him; but the imitator was a bit mixed in his super-sporting jargon; once I heard him exclaim, as he knocked my hat off the banister post, 'stick 'em up, buddy!'

There was John Foord dancing round the cream-washed bedroom pursued by Windles Neusel, who in the intervals when his opponent's pyjama trousers fell down around his ankles, turned aside and pounded John's shapeless bedclothes in exultant fury.

I felt I would like to join in the fun. But first I must, in the interests of good sportsmanship, reduce my stature. my head must be lowered for Windles's gloves to reach. First a cork was burnt in a candle flame; then pyjama jacket was thrown off and on my chest were drawn two eyes, a nose, and a wide grinning mouth. 'Coo, sporty!' cried Windles, squaring up to the effigy.

After breakfast I said we must go out, to get all the sun we could. Margaret didn't want to come very much, she said, there was a meet of foxhounds, and she wanted to see the hunters 'go trit-trot'. Margaret's dream was of herself 'trit-trotting' on a pony. For Christmas she had had a black velvet riding-cap, with peak and ribbon bow, just like the huntsman's cap. The thought of my promise coming true—that one day she should have a pony of her own, when she could wear her riding-cap—made her glow with joy. (Poor Margy, weeks and months, and alas, years went on, and no pony came; Father always too busy, or too selfish maybe; and the riding-cap became too small to be worn, and Robbie broke her riding-whip, another present, bought for 1s. at a jumble sale, and lost it.)

Margaret waited behind by the gate, wearing her riding-cap, somewhat self-consciously. She was used to being jeered at by the two bigger boys. And as John and Windles and I set off, there was Robert, hurrying out of the nursery, blue eyes wide with anxiety lest he be left behind. 'I-I-I-I'll tell 'ee suthing,' he began anxiously; 'you be gwin vor take me a ride in your car-car.'

'Us ban't going in car-car,' explained John. 'Us be going for a walk. A long walk, ever so far away-away.'

'No you ban't!' cried Robert. He looked up to our faces. 'I'll—I'll tell 'ee suthing!' he began again, with desperate hope in his blue eyes. 'You ban't going in car-car, be 'ee? Noo-oo! You be going only for a walk, ban't 'ee?' We waited with apprehension. 'Yes, 'tes only a walk you be going, ban't it?' He smiled at everyone and shook the golden curls which swept his shoulders. Then, with renewed anxiety, 'Robbie can come too, can't 'ee?'

'It's a long way-away walk, Robbie,' I said. At that, his mouth dropped and quivered. Quickly Margaret came to the rescue. 'Sister will take you to see kip-kips, Robbie,' she said, and began to heave him bodily on to her thin little knees as she sat on the log by the gate. The six-year-old child was only a few pounds heavier than her baby brother, but she made up for it with motherly spirit. 'Kip-kips go trit-trot, Robbie. You stay with sister and see kip-kips.' Tears hung on the lids of the tragic blue eyes turned up to mine. 'I'll let you ride my pony one day, Robbie,' whispered Margaret.

'Us wull feed our kip-kip one day, us wull!' cried Robert, his face happy once more. 'Us don't want vor go a walk, do us, Margy? Noo-oo! Us will see kip-kips, won't us? Coo, sporty!'

Leaving them to their dreams, the elder boys and I went up the steep path through the spruce and larch plantations of Bremridge Wood, every step removing the mental burdens that all house-bound men and women carry within themselves. Soon the layers of wood-smoke from the chimneys lay far below. It was a different world on top of the hill; the world of one's spirit and the sun. Perhaps they are indivisible. A pigeon was having a dust- and sun-bath on the path before us; it flew up with wings smacking together over its head. Past the farm, once the manor-house of the Fortescues, and up a stony track to higher ground, to warmer, greener grassland. At the corner of the field was a rare sight: a mole lying asleep in a tussock of rough grass. It was lying on its side, one pink shovel of a hand over its ear, as though listening in its sun-doze for possible enemies.

When it heard or felt our footfalls it rolled over and waddled away at a great rate, tumbling over itself in its eagerness to get to its tunnel. Mole-heaps of fresh earth showed where it had been mining. We ran forward, and I caught it, knowing its mouth and teeth were too small to bite my fingers. How strong it was! Held in two hands, it pushed its snout between them and almost pulled itself through by those shovel-paws. It was soft and sleek, with dark bluish-black fur. Its snout was red. We could hardly see its eyes.

'Just like pin-points, aren't they?' said Windles.

We looked for its ear-holes, but could not see them. All this time the mole was squeaking in my hands, thrusting and trying to get away.

I put him on the grass, first taking care to see that he was not near any of his tunnels. With those heavy, horny shovel-paws he tore himself through the matted grasses. Whenever I touched him, he turned and squeaked and struck at my fingers with one or another of his forepaws. The blow was a hefty one. 'Cor, sporty!' said Windles. 'Mole's tough, just like Neusel.'

'Cor, yes,' said John.

An experiment was suggested, while Windles held it. 'Go on, hold Mole, he won't hurt you. Look, I'll dig a bit of a hole—so! Now put him in and watch the grass flying!'

Mole scraped and dug, and soon was half-underground. I touched him with a finger, and now that he knew the unknown enemy had little power to harm him, he reversed and came out and with an angry little squeal 'gave me a proper dapp', in John's words. 'He's tisky,' said Windles, using a word much in vogue at the village school at that time. I began to tickle its ribs, and it paused, as though perplexed.

'Look,' cried Windles, pointing to a worm moving out from the grass a foot away from the tunnelling.

'Cor, he's travelling!' said John, admiringly. Obviously poor Worm was alarmed; long and pink, sharp-headed, it was drawing its innocent and sensitive length away from the terror.

'Let's give it the worm.'

'Oh no, Dad,' cried John and Windles together.

'I bet you Mole would eat it right away if you put it near,' I said, to tease them. I have a natural sympathy for earthworms, which turn fallen blossoms, dead leaves, and dead rootlets into beautiful mould.

'I'll sock you if you do,' muttered Windles, as he came close and tapped my ribs with his clenched fists. This was the boy who, a few days before, had thrown worms into the river from the bridge, wondering if the salmon kelts below would take them. And who, the previous night, had shot me with an imaginary machine-gun.

'It is a lovely streamline job, that worm, isn't it? And Mole is pretty cute, too. Don't let's interfere, that's a good idea of yours, Windles. Let them both get away, shall we?'

The south wind was blowing white clouds across the blue sky, the clover plants in the grass were a tender green, and we didn't get home until evening. For, lured by the sun, we went on for several miles, and finding a bus, got into it and let it take us to the end of its journey —which was twenty miles away.

Threshing

We were exploring. The earth was young again. As we went down a lane, we heard a humming sound on the wind. We saw smoke blown away in the wind, and then over the hedge, beside a group of ricks, the tall funnel of a steam-engine. On one of the stacks two men were standing, with pitchforks in their hands, while one fed the sheaves, their binding twine cut, into the drum of the threshing machine.

Windles's reaction to this sight was a question to John. 'Do you think Neusel could knock that thresher over with one punch?'

After serious reflexion, 'Coo, I dare say, if he had a mind to, and if he was strong enough,' which seemed to indicate that John had a judicial mind.

We went into the farmyard. Men and children and dogs were busy. Dead rats lay about. A terrier was scratching at a hole in the bank under the hedge. Two cattle dogs were watching, bright-eyed, the litter of straw and faggots which had made the base of one of the stacks just threshed.

Windles and John went at once to the steam-engine, with its polished fly-wheel turning with such smooth ease. A long endless belt was travelling between the fly-wheel and a pulley on the side of the thresher. The pulley was on the shaft of the interior drum, which revolved with humming speed and knocked the corn out of the ears as soon as the sheaves were dropped in above. We walked round the threshing-machine and put our hands into the sacks, catching the streams of wheat pouring into them. Windles asked why there were four streams and four sacks, and the sack-man told him to catch each stream in the palm of his hand in turn, examine the corn, and then he would learn the reason. Windles and John did this, and saw that the first two streams were the best, or head corn; while the third was made up of smaller, irregular berries, called tail-corn; and the fourth was mostly broken bits, mixed up with weed seeds.

One of the men came down from the stack to have a drink of cold tea from a bottle, and we noticed how the dust and straw specks were in his hair and on his face. As soon as he had had his drink, he climbed up and began pitching again. All were working their hardest to get the threshing done in the fine weather. Also, the farmer paid ten shillings an hour for the use of the tackle.

As the next stack got lower, so excitement in children and dogs increased. Windles and John had a stick each, and were practising swipes at imaginary rats.

'I say, Dad,' said Windles, 'let's pretend we're going to start a farm, shall we?'

'All right.'

'When we start our farming,' said Windles, 'we will have one of those engines, won't we?'

'I'm afraid we shan't be able to afford one. You see, a farmer can't afford a machine that he's only going to use three or four days a year. If we had a very big farm, or lots of farms, and could use it for many months a year, then it might pay for itself by the work it did.'

'I see what you mean,' said Windles, somewhat unhappily. 'Only I thought that if you pretended you had a farm, and you had a threshing-engine, I might drive it for you,' with a glance at the driver up aloft. The greasy peak of the driver's cap was half over one ear. The peak of Windles's cap was half over one ear. Windles was in a dream of pulling levers; blowing the whistle; he imagined himself spending his life, in blue and gold weather watching the fly-wheel turning so smoothly, so powerfully. He was living in an illusion of himself going from farm to farm, watching the steam- and water-gauges, cracking up the coal in the bunker, a bit of cotton-waste to wipe his hands on, a bottle of cold tea to drink from.

I thought of other places, other cornfields, always in blue and gold weather. *The wheat was orient and immortal corn* . . . until the sudden severance of August 1914, the corrosion of hope, which is illusion, to the bitter dark of death. And after those four years, the bitter dark of men's minds, the same system of struggle for markets in Europe, the same war arising inevitably if the system were not entirely altered: Windles and John leaving home with another British Expeditionary Force. . . .

'What's the matter, Dad, anything I said?'

'Yes, it must be lovely to go about to various farms, threshing the corn. Better even than driving the Silver Link, don't you think?'

'I suppose a modern one would be streamlined?' he asked doubtfully. 'And work a bit better than this old sort?'

'I don't think there are any modern ones, Windles. Steam is out of date, for this sort of work, anyway. A tractor could drive this thresher just as well.'

'Shall we pretend to have a tractor on our farm? But honestly, Dad, was it anything I said that upset you?' This was a new Windles. And yet, was it new? Was it not the same boy who showed such anxiety that the old spaniel, long since dead, should come out of the road when a motor car was heard approaching?

At that moment the engine whistled. 'Of course, a tractor can't whistle, can it?'

'You're laughing at me, Dad!'

'Well, we could easily fit a four-note whistle on the exhaust that would be heard right across Devon.'

'Cor, John!' cried Windles. 'Dad says we can have a four-note whistle on the exhaust of our new tractor.'

A shout from behind made us turn round and hurry to where three dogs were pressing their heads into the straw. 'Coo, I saw a master great rat,' said John, his cheeks pink with excitement. 'Do you think if I gave it a dapp with this stick I could kill it? Windles has killed a rat, but I haven't killed one yet.'

One of the dogs yelped with excitement, and jumped up on its hind legs to get a view over the straw. A sudden outburst of barking round the other side of the stack drew a rush of dogs and children. There, running a zigzag course over the straw, was a mouse. There must have been twenty children, shouting and striking at it, while the dogs tumbled over one another, barking and yelping. One grey sheepdog snapped it up, and swallowed it immediately.

'What a nasty thing,' said a little girl. 'I don't like that dog, eating mice like that.'

'Well, haven't you eaten part of a sheep?' inquired Windles.

'But 'er don't go gobbling it up raw,' cried John.

There was another shout. This time a black dog snapped a rat as it ran out, shook it hard for about a second, and then dropped it dead. A terrier ran up to the rat, gave it a quick sniff, and turned away. The threshing-machine went on humming, smoke and steam blowing away from the engine, and grey clouds with hard edges moved over the farmyard from the north-west. I was thinking that I wished I'd put on a warmer jacket, when three half-grown rats ran out among the children, who shrieked and tried to get away, some falling over. The dogs ran amongst them, a sheepdog taking a leap right over one child who was picking itself up. Almost instantly, it seemed, the three rats were dead and forgotten. When the stack-men got down to the faggots at the base of the stack, the fun became, in Windles's word, tisky. Rats and mice ran out in every direction, pursued by a shrill mob of children striking at them with sticks. Heedless of the thumps of sticks the dogs leapt and darted in and out of the children, sometimes knocking a small one down as they nipped and shook and dropped and dashed about for more.

At the end of the rat-hunt, when things had slowed down, a boy appeared from behind the thresher, holding a mouse by the tail.

'Ha ha hi!' he shouted, and immediately all the children ran to him and began to shout. But not Windles. He stood apart. I knew what he felt, for his feelings were mine. Fifteen children shouting at the tops of their voices, *jeering* at one wretched little animal trying to climb up its own body, while the boy swung it round and round by its tail, and others struck at it with the tips of their sticks. The look on Windles's face was half-sullen, half-scornful. Seeing him, the big boy went up to him and dangled the mouse before his face. The other children screamed with delight. Windles looked wildly about him, having some of the feelings of a hunted animal. Then as the high jeering of the children seemed to increase he went white. The boy flicked the mouse in his face. 'Come on!' shouted Windles, as he clenched his fists and squared up to his tormentor. Perhaps the mouse would escape after all, in the mix-up of dogs and children—in which was Windles with flashing eyes and tangled hair, wrestling with the bigger boy. I went between them and pulled them apart, and as I did so the man on the engine blew a blast on the whistle.

The long belt between engine and thresher was now turning very slowly. Windles got up.

'Coo, I saw the mouse run off,' said John, admiringly.

'Shut up,' growled Windles, as he walked past John. As he passed the engine the man called to him.

'Proper,' he said. 'That was my boy you were pasting; 'twill do him good.'

Windles mumbled something about not having hit him.

'Would you like to stop my engine?' said the driver.

'I don't know how to.'

'I'll show 'ee, midear,' said the driver.

'Yes, please,' said Windles. 'I would very much like to stop it.'

'Put your foot on that step, and up you get. Now pull this yurr lever back.'

The dark glistening fly-wheel, which had been flicking round so smoothly, gave a sigh, and came to rest.

'Would you like to blow the whistle?'

'Yes, please,' said Windles.

'Pull that string.'

The whistle screeched.

'Thank you very much,' said Windles, getting down from the cab.

'You ought to shake hands with that boy and make friends with him,' I said.

'All right,' said Windles, and went up to the boy. They shook hands.

The engine-driver called out in a gruff voice to his son, 'Did you get my beer as I told 'ee?' He winked at me.

'Yes, Father,' said the boy, smiling at Windles, who smiled back at him.

12

Wind, Sand and Sea

With the spring came the east winds; and one Saturday morning A'Bess and I, taking John (Windles being on a visit to cousins in Surrey) set out for a walk along sands by the estuary. We motored as far as the great new white hotel awaiting its hundred and fifty Easter guests, and leaving the Silver Eagle, went down by the steep path to the beach. The boy held my hand. An old cap of mine was on his head, the peak pulled over an ear. Under the cap long fair hair stuck out.

We walked south, along the top of the strand, just short of the line of dunes, crowned by marram grass, where the going was fairly firm, and there was some sort of shelter from a strong east wind, which was whipping dry sand across the wet shore towards the dirty brown wavelets half a mile away to the west. I had walked along this shore in the past many times by myself, and later with a spaniel dog; then with Loetitia, before we were married. Now I had beside me our second son, seven years of age. Such changes during the years! I felt myself to be middle-aged, the best part of life to be over —very soon I should be forty years of age. A man almost done for! (Almost a quarter of a century later, as I revise this book, I feel much younger than I did at the time of which I write.)

We had some bread and cheese and fruit in a rucksack, and did not envy the people from the towns, sitting behind all that glass of the great sitting-room—the 'lounge' it was called—with their central heating and polished floors. We were with the wind and the sand; we were adventurers, we were going exploring, on a far journey, weren't we, John?

'Coo, yes!'

The seven-year-old by my side, with elfin face and haystack hair, began to consider the skeins of sand lodging against the edges of our shoes.

'Supposin' us gets buried by a huge enormous storm, what will us do until they finds our bones?' he asked, his eyes alight with the memory of some story in the children's section of the newspaper he pounced upon and read so eagerly every Saturday morning.

'Well, if this wind keeps up, and the sandhills cover us completely, they may never find even our bones.'

'Then you and me will be proper skeletons, won't us?' adding to himself in a musing undertone, 'I'd bestways eat my apples and chocolate biscuits first.' And then to me, 'But the sandhills won't really move, will they?'

'They are moving all the time. Look over there, the sand is pouring away from it.'

'It's like a waterfall, isn't it? Oh, some sand got in my mouth. It's a good thing us didn't bring Baby Robert after all, isn't it, because he would not only get sand in his mouth, but in his ears and eyes, wouldn't he?'

As usual, Robert had climbed into the motor car that morning and gripped the wheel, stricken with anguish at not being allowed to come. He punched and slapped and screamed oaths at me as I detached him from the seat. 'Would you like a chocolate bikky?' I said to him, as he tried to start the engine.

'Six,' he promptly replied, and when I gave him one, he threw it on the ground. 'I'll have six,' he decided, as the farmer's dog Towser crunched it up. So he had six—which to Robert still meant one in each hand. The last we saw of him as we went round the corner was a little child lying huddled-up in the lane outside the garage, sobbing with his face in his arms, and shaking his yellow curls, which still lay upon his shoulders, as the gentle voice of his mother invited him indoors to have an apple—or rather six apples, for Robert was seldom content with one of anything.

At the end of this book, I intend to tell how these children turned out when they grew up; meanwhile, as we walked upon Santon Sands that day, John and I agreed that it was a good thing that Baby Robert had been left behind, as the risping sand skirled faster over the shore from the ragged sandhills. The white warren on the cliffs behind us grew smaller, as hand in hand we went on towards Airy Point. It was a rasping east wind, returning to ocean sand which a thousand centuries of waves had ground from rock and pebble and shell, and innumerable south-west gales had driven inland before them.

Once this coast had been part of the old river bed; and when the river had moved away to the south, trees had sprung up from acorns and other seeds brought down by winter floods to lie on shoal and rotted leaf-bank. It was said that a forest once covered the shore and the sandhills in olden times, the roaming place of moose and red deer, preyed on by wolves, and the dreadful sabre-toothed tiger. Less than three miles from where we were walking, across the estuary the carbonized roots of trees could still be seen at low tide, embedded in sand. Men digging there had found the bones of all those animals.

The east wind was a destructive wind, a wide drift of icy air then crossing Europe from Siberia. How different was the wind from the south-west: a genial, boisterous wind, adding to the sandhills until they were smoothed, fluted, and crenellated as by an artist, except where bound by the marram grass, whose hollow stems, when not swaying or rippling, drew upon the sand arcs and circles with their sharp points.

All winds were enemies of marram grass. The western edges of the dunes were in place cliff-like, exposed roots of the grass hung ragged down sandy faces which, before the winter's storms, had been smooth slopes where naked feet had sunk to the ankle at every step in the hot sands of summer. Then the sands purred under the moving feet, as one trudged across a luminous desert, where all sense of time and place was lost under the sky, the explorer become a spirit of sea and air, free in the everlastingness of life while larks sang shrilly overhead and the bones and skulls of rabbits lying upon the shimmering slopes were of a glowing whiteness.

Now, on a March day, the Siberian wind drove the sand to prick our ankles through socks and stockings. It was a wild scene of almost visible despair. Trunks and roots of trees, washed down the rivers in flood, then to be worn by the churn of waves on gravel and rock, lay half-buried at the top of the tide-line, with rusty tins, feathers, corks, skeletons of dead birds, some with tufts of feathers brown with oil-fuel still upon the bones, an occasional skull of a sheep, a swede turnip which somehow looked sadly out of place, glass bottles which the sand-blast had ground to a dull opaqueness. Hand in hand we walked on, heads averted from the east; below us, over livid wet sands, the broken white lines of grey sea. Thence we began to wonder what strange object it was that lay before us at the top of the tide line. It was like a man sitting up, leaning against a pile of sand; and from it, as we drew nearer, came a queer aerial music, as though it were playing to itself. But by now we saw it was no human figure, but the stump of a tree. What could it be? Then walking round to the other side of the mass of wood we saw hundreds of barnacles clinging there; their fragile grey shells, hanging upon dried and shrunken pipes, were tinkling in the wind. While we listened to this chiming of sea-shells there came through the wind another sound, not unlike that of a flung stone whimpering across ice. John pointed to a small grey-and-white bird with sharp wings, flying round us in a wide circle. It was a ringed plover, one of a small colony which lived all the year round upon this shore. We saw its mate running before us among the stones and loose sand above the tide-line: the bird stopped, to stand gravely to watch us, before running on again as though to draw us away from the dreamed-on place where her eggs would be laid, somewhere in a slight hollow amidst the stones, in the coming spring: four eggs the colour of sand, stone, and dried seaweed, for which one might look all day and never find.

We walked on, leaving the slight shelter of the sand-hills to look at the timbers of a wooden ship embedded in the sands below us. This was the first wreck John had seen. He studied it gravely, before suggesting that we should come back here in summer with buckets and spades and dig for the gold which, he declared, might be buried beneath it.

'It might have been a pirate ship, mightn't it? Anyways, I would best-ways like to bathe by this one in summer, so us must come back even if it ban't a pirate ship after all. And us must bring Robbie to see it, mus'n't us, and all the other children?'

The hotel on the cliff, far away behind us, was now a small elongated white honeycomb. Perhaps the visitors were still watching the sea and sky through the windows, and wondering if they too ought not to go down to the sands and defy the wind. Or were they eating luncheon?

'Are you hungry, John?'

'Yes, I be,' with an upward smile of the peaked face. So we moved upshore again into the shelter of the sand-hills, noticing how strewn dry sand was lying behind every stone, stick, and shell lying on the shore, giving each object its streamline. The sand-grains had found shelter there, in the wind-eddies, I told John, who was now, with arms outstretched, pretending to be lifted on the winds like a gull.

We found a sandy cliff where the sun was warm and the wind did not turn in eddy, and dug ourselves holes to sit in; and there the child drank his milk and we ate our food.

We were still some way from the estuary, where we hoped to see salmon boats; but John having declared that he was not tired, we set out once more into the sweep of the wind, having folded up our sandwich paper to take it home, not to add to the fading summer litter on the beach. Going down towards the sea to find firmer sand, we saw a beetle hurrying downwind as fast as it could move.

'Oh,' cried the boy, staring at it. 'If it goes on thissy way it will get to the sea and then it will have to turn round and run all the way back! 'Tes one mile there, and one mile back, that will be two miles!' He stared at me with round eyes.

I suggested that we turn it back; but at the touch of a finger up went its tail; and the wind caught the little black sail and skidded it a couple of yards before it found its feet again, to hurry on to escape its enemy, the wind. What could we do to save it? There it was, hurrying on to destruction.

'Well, perhaps a sea-trout will find it and eat it, and that's something.'

On we trudged, passing a small red tower standing at the edge of the sandhills, called the Blinker by sailors, because at night the oil lamp in its lantern winked towards the sandbars at the mouth of the estuary, giving river pilots a bearing. It was obvious that the Blinker had been needed on that coast, for we came upon two more wooden wrecks sunken in sand, seaweed hanging upon timbers from which the iron trenails had long since rusted.

The sand where we were now walking was uneven, giving way to patches of shingle, telling that the tides ran strongly around Airy Point. Now the low shore of the estuary was just visible, edged with black fragments which as we crossed the curve of sand with its slight mirage resolved into the forms of men and boats at the edge of leaden water. We hurried forward, because these were the boats we had come to see, and the tide had turned, and they would not be able to fish there much longer, it being a spring tide, one of the lowest-and-highest of the year, with strong ebb and flow. So we ran, hand in hand, lest we miss the great sight we had come to see.

I had seen the manner of fishing many times, but to the

child it was all new and wonderful. They were still fishing when we reached the water. One man of each crew of four held the rope on shore, while two men rowed the boat in a semicircle, the fourth man throwing the net over the stern.

'I bags that boat,' said John, pointing to No. 27. I chose No. 4. Which would catch fish first?

No. 27 set out to shoot its draught first. It came back to shore when the 200-yard net had been dropped, then began the slow haul-in against the weight of the tide. The wind was very cold now that we stood still, so we helped to haul. And then, as the tide-distorted arc of the net grew smaller, we stood apart and watched. There was a swirl as the purse came near the shore; at once the men seemed to change their natures, becoming almost Spanish in the quick and eager way they spoke. I told John the legend was that many of the fishermen in the village across the water had Spanish blood in them, from ancestors who had been wrecked on the coast after the defeat of the Spanish Armada in 1588. For usually the blue-eyed crews of salmon boats did not show excitement over fish in the net; they hauled in stolidly as before, it was nothing unusual to them. Or these dark-eyed men may have been new to fishing, and elated after blank draughts with the net so far; there had been no fish in their boat. The skipper told them to take it easy, so that the heel-rope, weighted with lead, should come in slowly along the bottom and give no chance for the fish to push underneath.

The purse was lifted up on to the gravel shore, and in it two salmon were slapping about. One man put his boot under a fish and kicked it away from the edge of the sea, where it heaved itself upright on its pectoral fins and tried to writhe down to the water. Meanwhile one of the crew of No. 4 boat, fifty yards away—the net of which was being hastily re-piled, since fish often came into the estuary in schools—had thrown a wooden billet through the air, and with this the fish were killed by blows on the neck. I felt them almost to be beating upon my own life, for after some years of meditation, I was about to start my book on the life of a salmon: the dream was about to be exposed to, or transformed into, another medium. Almost the terrors of a beetle in the sea were behind my mind: failure. But such thoughts must not be allowed to destroy the *trauma*, the dream of the ring plover among her stones.

The crew of No. 4 was now hauling in silently, and fast; that of No. 27 shaking clear their net of stones, weed, and crabs, ready to re-pile and shoot again. Another of the dark men gave a shout, having seen a fish leap near the shore. Up-estuary, No. 4 had taken fish. The sweeps of No. 27 were bent as the boat cleft the water. When the net was hauled in, there was one fish in it, about eighteen pounds; a sow-fish, like the other two. Female fish usually preceded the males, called keepers, in spring. The females were more slender and graceful in shape than the males, having smaller heads; their underjaws did not, as summer changed to autumn, develop the kypes, or hooked lower jaws, of the keepers.

I noticed, as I had before, that salmon when taken in a net seemed to struggle with only part of their power, as though still dreamy from the deeps of ocean—pale green travellers from rocky glooms of undersea twilight, perhaps from under the steep shelf where Europe broke off, below the south coast of Ireland, and yielded to the ocean-god.

John entered my reverie by whispering, 'Maybe the fishermen will give us one of the salmon if I tell them that they might be some of the smolts which were born in our river at home.'

'But the fishermen must sell fish to buy food and clothes for their children. Now for that big fish there, eighteen pounds in weight, they will get thirty-six shillings.'

'Thirty-six shillings!' he repeated. 'Why, that's an awful lot of money, isn't it? They must be rich, mus'n't they?'

I explained that perhaps it was the first fish to be shared by the crew of four that week, and also, there was a licence of £5 to be paid every season, which lasted only until the end of August; and perhaps somebody else owned the net and boat and so had shares with the crew. The fishermen did not always get enough to pay their way.

'Well,' he whispered in my ear, 'I have got some pennies at home, and perhaps us could find out if they don't catch any more fish and us could give them my pennies, couldn't us?'

The wind had a cutting edge as we turned back that afternoon, the sun was behind clouds, the fishermen going home on the tide; and before us was all the way back along the sands, the boy's feet growing heavier and heavier, apples and biscuits and figs all eaten, milk-bottle empty; so on to Father's back, with thoughts of returning in the summer, when the wind was gone, and the sands shining, and 'Us'll dig for that treasure underneath the wreck, with all the other children'. It was always 'all the other children' with John when he was happy, or had chocolate: thin little body, narrow shoulders, soft voice: all gentleness, and no fear at all, as far as I could see; not ordinary fear, or rather ordinary effects of fear: for John always stood his ground. The child slept upon my back, dreaming of treasure in the silver of waves, in the golden glance of the sun.

13

Life Catches Up

Closing the iron gates of the deer park behind me with a clang, tired and wet after working in the river—or rather trying to undo some of my work, for I had planted water-buttercup some years before, it had spread in geometrical progression, and now threatened to ruin all the fishing rights for miles below me—I went along the garden path of the cottage. A candle shining in the dining-room window, shadowy forms of Windles and his mother sitting at the refectory table. They were frowning over a piece of printed paper.

'What's the matter?'

'Oh, it's only these examination questions,' replied Loetitia. 'Some are rather difficult. But he's getting along all right, I think.'

Examination papers? *My* little boy going in for an examination? Good heavens . . . he was growing up!

'How old are you?'

'Eleven, Father.'

'Eleven?'

'He's trying for a scholarship to a secondary school.'

Children are children. Children being children do not grow up—until suddenly in a parent's eyes. Our life had, until now, seemed to be timeless. The seasons came, and went, only to return, as before; as the children had gone to the village school, had holidays, only to return, as before.

It was almost a shock.

So that was the explanation of these two sitting, night after night, side by side at the table gleaming darkly beyond the little shine of a candle! Soon the boy would be a youth: the pathetic frowns and perplexities were the beginning of a young man's world.

I looked at the questions. They were the same sort of questions I had tried to answer in those days which for an eternity of time I had been thinking of as the Old World, the pre-1914 world.

'Windles can't do "hard sums",' said Loetitia, looking as though she couldn't do 'hard sums' herself, which in fact was the case.

'Let's have a look.'

> A room the walls of which are 20 feet long, 18 feet wide, and 8 feet high, has to be papered. The window spaces are 6 feet wide and 4 feet deep, the door is 7 feet high and 4 feet wide, the fireplace is of brick and its outside dimensions are 5 feet by 4 feet. The wall-paper to be used is in rolls 2 feet wide, and is to be hung from ceiling to floor, allowing for windows, fireplace and door. Allowing 50 feet in a roll, what is the minimum number of rolls required?

'I can't do "hard sums", either!'

Windles stared anxiously from face to face.

'That's the sort of rubbish by which my brain used to

be perplexed, and my nervous system assailed, when I was a child! If a boy can't do it, the inability gives him a sense of inferiority, driving his natural intelligence inwards, making him introspective. I thought that mind-despoiling, tread-mill kind of education had gone in the Great War. Anyhow, why should he need a scholarship?'

'Well, if he remains at the village school—' murmured Loetitia. And added, sighing, 'It's rather a problem, isn't it?'

The problems of writing were hard enough . . . but I was thinking selfishly, I was a father of four male children, who would sooner or later become four adolescents to be settled in life. Vaguely I had thought, or put off the thought, of their education. Some time in the past their names had been put down for a West Country school, although I had doubted if there would be enough money to pay the fees when the time came. If not (my idle fancy had run) they would remain at the village school, learn to read and write, and receive their education from me. The basis of this education was to have been work in the open air. If at the age of eighteen they were deficient in self-confidence, poise, good manners, graciousness, strong bodies, natural ease in all contacts with their fellow men, determination, punctuality, and ability to act efficiently and reliably in whatsoever kind of work each young man wanted to do—well, the fault would be entirely mine. All young creatures, whether men or animals, learned by imitation. Speech, accent, the way to behave towards others, the formula or technique of doing a job of work economically—that is, to do it artistically, with pleasure—all would be imitated from me, the father, and those working with me.

All would be imitated from me.

And what a model! What had they learned from me? A number of oaths, as inoculation against swearing in later life; to shout at their mother and other women in the house; unpunctuality at meals; the life of Cold Pudding; to trespass on the viaduct of the Great Western Railway in order to launch paper sailplanes from that dizzy place; to tell the truth and not to be afraid of grown-up people.

I had, partly, put an old (and not altogether admirable) head on young shoulders, in other words, unaware of the saying, *An old head on young shoulders has to be knocked off.* I had filled them with ideas which probably would not apply to circumstances of their world. At the moment, tired after hauling at tons of river weed, ever-conscious of the possibility of legal action for damaging valuable fishing-rights down as far as the tide-head miles away, I felt depressed.

The next evening, coming up the garden path, after scything and releasing about a couple of tons of weed, again I saw the heads of mother and son together in the candle-light. 'Don't worry if you can't get through those barbed-wire obstacles you call "hard sums",' I told him, as he frowned and squirmed on the oak form. 'Arithmetic should be called Bewilderment and Complication for the Young. The system, anyhow, is based on ignorance, on the belief that mental wrestling, as my old Head Master used to call it, develops the mind. I do not believe that it is good. Being bored and bewildered and forcing the attention improves no nervous system. The brain is a nervous system. Don't lie awake at night, dreading you won't get a scholarship.'

The gist of my further remarks—I give them now, without enthusiasm, for the record—was that the system would be altered before he was a man; and he would never feel inferior in later life because he didn't go to a public school, or a secondary school, or because he didn't know a word of Latin or Greek, or the difference between *sine* and *cosine* in trigonometry, or those equivalents of the crossword puzzle among certain idle intelligentsia of an extinct civilization called the figures of Euclid. If, when his brain was fully grown, those and similar subjects interested him, then he'd take to them easily; meanwhile it was his father's idea and business to see that the sun and air and food of England built him a natural body and natural mind.

Even so, at that time one had an uneasy feeling that it was an avoidance of the problem. If the ideas were true, they would be made material some time in the future; meanwhile, what of the present?

I thought of my friends in London, who worked in offices. They worked there to make money, and dreamed of eventually escaping from office life to a living in the country. They thought I was fortunate, and courageous, to have left London after the war and without money to have gone to the remote country, with full hope and belief in myself as a writer. It wasn't courage to have quit a distasteful life in London; it was running away. But I had had confidence in my ability to earn my living in the country; I was my own master. But now the idyllic period of the children's lives was about to end and material problems must be faced.

About this time I went to visit a friend in another part of England, and returned with an idea. The next day my eldest son and I went for a walk, leaving the valley below us. We walked on the moor. There, in the sun and the west wind, it seemed that my idea was possible: I was still young enough to work hard and continuously, to believe that, by will-power, one could succeed in anything. In the light of nature, I believed that only the country could give a man knowledge; that the townsman could only have that secondary thing, learning. I believed that true knowledge, apart from research, was that learnt by the body used in harmony with the mind: that the brain was only a control-tower and reference library. Intuition was a living thing, and the source of intuition was the land. A man cutting and laying a hedge, a man driving a furrow, a man observing how a bullock tears away its bite with its tongue wrapped round grass, while a sheep nibbles close and thereby ruins a balanced pasture if allowed too long on it; or a man singing on a windy, cloud-and-sunshine rushing day of spring as he harrows clover in the barley stubble—that man lived naturally, his knowledge was part of his spirit; not apart from his life.

A lark was singing in the sky, the grass was shining in the west wind.

'What would you like to be, Windles, when you grow up?'

'I'd like to be a farmer, Dad.'

'A farmer? The finest work on earth! Let's take a farm,' I said, jokingly.

'Do you mean it, Dad? Really?'

Did I mean it? Well, I hadn't really meant it, it was only an idea. A farm! In another part of England, entirely different from the west!

Farming was depressed, now was the time to begin! I would have a new subject to write about; I could earn money by my pen at night, while working in the open air all day. The land needed someone to cry out for it, all the men leaving the land, England filled with foreign food because of the capitalization of foreign countries with British money, unrestricted export of sterling to employ sweated, cheap foreign labour to undercut home industry, and put millions on the dole; the land of Britain decaying, the mother of our race losing fertility!

To the urbanized mind of the intellectual the plowman, sitting still on a bench with a pot of beer beside him in the village pub at night, was a dull, crude sort of fellow. How could they know that Hodge was a craftsman, an expert within the limits of his natural capabilities, and that he sat still because he was truly relaxed after a natural day's work? He was deeply content; they, poor souls, were seeking, in talkies and intellectualism, for the natural formula of fulfilment and happiness. Only in the body working in harmony with the brain could natural happiness be found. Sooner or later the basis of children's education would be the land, when the 'hard sums' idea would be gone with all other ideas of an exhausted and effete system.

Windles, to my surprise, won a scholarship to a boarding school a few miles away from where we lived. Thither he was due to go in the following September. Meanwhile we had given notice to quit Shallowford at Michaelmas, in a year's time.

14

Seven-Year Cycle

I often wish I had kept a diary of the weather since 1921, when I came to live in North Devon. In that year there was a prolonged drought, with no rain falling between April and August, and many grazing fields were brown and dusty. In 1927 there was a hard winter, when both Taw and Torridge nearly froze from bank to bank in places; and the next year a gale swept from the west and thousands of trees, many of them elms, were thrown, some across roads. I remember, motoring to London a few days afterwards in my open Morris Minor, counting thirteen trees in one field of seven acres near Langport in Somerset, all of them lying parallel, and pointing to the north-west. Along the way to London clotted root-clumps were to be seen horizontal in fields—trees literally torn out of the ground. Even oaks, which have the strongest tap-roots, were pushed over by the wind against their branches. Some of the trunks were cracked across, so violent their fall, or possibly due to the wrenching, with creaks and groans, before the final shriek-like rending apart.

Then there was the very wet year of 1932, when it rained in the valley of the Bray, and elsewhere, during forty-three week-ends. Freshet followed freshet over the falls and down upon the rocks and gravel-beds, under the alders, all during the summer. I was reminded of this the other day when I asked Loetitia if I was, during our life together at Shallowford, more or less reliable as regards time. She said, 'Well, I remember the occasion when you set out for church one Sunday and came back three days later.'

I had entirely forgotten this, and asked her if she could remember where I had been.

'Oh, you arrived late at church, so went on to the field, then you took part in a yacht race at Instow, then you went on to see friends on Dartmoor, from what you said when you came back. We were rather alarmed, as the river was running bank-high, and we thought perhaps you had fallen in and been swept away.'

'What an awful person I must have been.'

'A little unpredictable at times,' smiled Loetitia.

The following winter was the driest I had known while in the valley. The river was down to lowest summer level from November to March. I remember seeing hundreds of bronze- and copper-coloured salmon—the females or sows, and the males or keepers—spawning in winter in water not deep enough to cover back-fins and tail-fin tops. Scores of dead kelts, spawned-out fish, were lying in the slow eddies at the tails of pools. The foxes and crows and rats had plenty to eat.

As for our last winter in the valley, I remember it for its fogs. On Christmas night I lay in bed unable to see anything, my eyes bandaged, writing with a pencil and feeling my way across the pad. The least glimmer of candle-light stabbed my eyeballs with pain. I had conjunctivitis, caused by smoke-acids, grit, and intense cold endured for some hours on the naked eyeballs.

Two days before I had been in London, having gone there on business, and was looking forward to Christmas at home with Loetitia and the children. There was no doubt whatsoever in me where my heart lay; and the centre of that heart was my hearth, and a vision of slippered feet stretched to the beech-log fire; I half-asleep while the children played in the next room, or came in around the armchair and roasted chestnuts. Or we played snakes and ladders, ludo, draughts, and dominoes. This was the vision in London, while thick, cold fog dissolved everything outside the club which was my home when in that town. Car and shop lights showed feebly, suddenly, as one groped a way about. The fog, newspapers said, lay over most of England, from the Humber to the Wash, and on down to the Thames estuary, along the south coast to the West Country and up to Wales and beyond to Liverpool and of course Manchester and its chimneys.

The roads were slippery with ice; visibility in places was nil; trains were running up to twelve hours late, and these conditions were forecast to extend over Christmas.

Having known that some weather prophecies had not been borne out by facts, I decided to wait a day, and travel down on Christmas Eve in the Silver Eagle—a fairly fast touring car in which I sat in an open cockpit with leather flying-helmet, goggles, gauntlets, and coat. But at night the rain did not come, with the wind; and in the morning it was darker than ever. I rang up the A.A. and they said that motor cars were stranded all over the country. They advised me not to start.

The prospect of staying alone in London, with the club closed on Christmas Day, was appalling. Christmas without the children! Truly was it said that we know the value of what we have only when we have lost it. After all, I was Father. Would they grieve without me? I certainly would grieve without them. I waited until nearly noon, and then rang the A.A. again. Thicker and colder than ever! Traffic at a standstill!

At least the roads would be open, I thought, and determined to start immediately.

At first light I drifted away from Adelphi Terrace—since alas, pulled down and replaced by a white concrete edifice —I think that is the right word—just off the Strand, to make my way to the safety of the Great West Road at Chiswick. The windscreen was fixed flat. The eyes watered, with acid and chemicals cast into them by forward movement. It was cold, despite leather coat, fur collar, and that 1915 fur-lined helmet. Goggles were useless; they misted up immediately.

Strange shapes and dim yellow points of light appeared almost on top of me from all directions, to vanish and be replaced by others, endlessly. My speed varied from 1 to 12 miles an hour, and I had 180 miles to go. I was forced through apprehension and despair to stop several times, feeling I could not go on.

Two and a quarter hours after starting I reached the Great West Road at Chiswick, and began to feel that I had got away from the worst; nevertheless I should have to go faster if I was to arrive home by daylight. Headlights in frozen mist would limit sight to the radiator; and it was doubtful if I should be able to see by side-lights. Yet I must get home for Christmas.

I was more hopeful as my speed increased to 20 m.p.h. A feeling of loneliness arose, which had to be resisted. I had the sensation of moving along the bed of the sea.

There were four more hours of this muffled daylight, in which one moved past abruptly-forming ghosts which dissolved almost soundlessly. I put on goggles when my eyes ached unendurably, and was tremendously elated to realize that the speed prevented them from misting up. I increased to 25 m.p.h. For another hour I felt my way along a dim ocean-bed, through drowned Staines, and onwards, passing submarine shapes with eyes moving suddenly upon me. I drove, as it were, by finger-tip. I was guiding a wheeled toboggan over patches of ice which swung about at the least unconfident touch on brake pedal or steering-wheel. I drove now without hesitation; my nerves no longer reacted. Life was hope and isolation in a dreamlike unreality. Ragged hedges passed away backwards in my dissolved existence.

And then in a sudden moment the sun, which briefly had appeared like a shining cocoon in the mist, broke in light upon my eyes, and I was in a new world, under a sky of azure that made me sing with joy.

It was a marvellous moment. I was alone on a blue and white planet. Tall hedges on either side glittered with hoar frost. The fields were entirely white. Every tree was a delicate grey shadow. Through the hedge on my left the sun flickered continually as I drove along, light rippling across my face and eyes. I loved it. I waggled the wheel, the car skidded, I shouted with sudden rage at myself as we nearly slithered into a ditch.

Sunshine softened the ice on the road, and we could with safety go faster, windscreen still flat, but goggles over eyes, keen air cutting my cheeks and filling me with joy of being alive, and the faith that now I should get home to Shallowford for Christmas. Faster, faster, for night would fall in the afternoon.

The road before Stockbridge raced to meet the tarnished Silver Eagle on the radiator cap at 70 m.p.h. We passed—this old companion with ninety-five synthetic horses and I—a burnt-out saloon lying on its side, frosty where the sun had not touched it; then a lorry tilted in a ditch. The blue sky spanned my world.

At Salisbury we stopped, the driver for roast beef and the engine for Castrol oil and Benzol mixture. Then on again, fast because the day would soon be gone. Across the Great Plain, a shroud of frost, the engine opened its heart to the screaming wind, and we rushed down to Mere and Wincanton, and were in Somerset, the next county to Devon and home!

We should soon be in Devon, it was not so distant by miles; but already it was nearly three o'clock, already ice was growing its mock roots across road plashes, already heavy white mist was gathering in the hollows of fields. Goggles now froze over, so the windscreen was raised. Almost at once ferns of ice grew upon the glass, layer upon layer. The wiper would not clear them. We had about eighty more miles to go, so putting the screen flat again, I pushed on as fast as I dared.

Then, as abruptly as we had gone from mist to sunlight that morning, we were in an occluded world, and frost was cutting flesh from cheek-bones, biting through gloves, scooping tears from eyes and gumming lashes of each lower lid together.

The car was a wheeled sledge. Soon pain ceased to be pain, as I moved on into blind space. My eyes were wet and semi-sightless sockets. Fingers, hands were made of wood. I was lost, I went on, somewhere presumably, driving by the dim grey hedges seen fixedly with each eyeball's retina. I stopped, pushed myself thickly out of my bucket seat, sought and found a cottage, and learned I was in Dorset, travelling south instead of west. I went back, swinging my arms, but could not find the car. It was lost; yet I had left it only a few yards away. It was a dead world, I the only thing moving upon or in it. I did not care. Then I saw the side-lights, tiny and weak, six feet in front of me. With gloved hands I pawed ineffectually at layers of ice a quarter of an inch thick on the windscreen. Icicle stubs were forming on the lower rim of the steering-wheel, and I wondered how they had got there. My face in the driving mirror was dirty, brick-red and swollen. The fur collar of my coat was clogged white. It was no use stopping. I had to go on, so I went on, having nothing else to do, into a glacial fog of twilight, the radiator hardly warm, the wheels slipping and sliding, the body sometimes brushing a hedge with its wings, and once scraping horridly along the wall of a cottage garden.

When it became too dark to see more than five feet ahead I turned on the headlights, to be totally confronted by their blindness. I switched off, pulled up my seat close to the steering-wheel and stood up. Then starting the engine again I put in the second gear and half standing went on like that, steering by a glimpse of both forward mudguards spaced as equally as possible between the hedges on either side of the unseen road, while trying to anticipate a turn by the disappearance of one or another of the hedges. Once I stopped from exhaustion and saw moving by me the slow phantoms of cows. It was almost as though my brain had sensed them without telling me. But I had had no prevision of cows, I had stopped by chance.

Darkness came with teatime, but I was now an automaton, moving forward into fog and frost, meeting no one, seeing nothing, hearing only the grind of the second gear.

At the beginning of the fourteenth hour out of London, as I stopped, about to get out to swing creaking leathered arms and to stamp my feet, I was startled to think that I had perceived rather than that I had seen, since my eyes had long been out of focus, a white gate and posts which were—could they be—the gates of the drive down to Mecca's? I dared not think I was mistaken as I drove on past rhododendrons until I stopped before the house and knew it for my friend's. Hardly knowing what to do I managed to pull first one leg then the other leg from the constricted space of the bucket seat fixed so far forward, and almost fell from the car, to recover and walk to the bell handle. Then I was going down a long passage and into a room, to see a ruddy smiling face and be given the best welcome in the world. Had he not made me the villain in one of his novels? And had I not returned the compliment? Literary villainy was outworn; but not hospitality. Clutching a large glass of whiskey, I peered at his hearth through closed lids, feeling the cold in me chilling the very flames of the fire. I swallowed another large glass of whiskey without effect. Then a wash, and food, the car put away among faggots, heavy feet lifting upstairs, too tired to remove clothes before dropping asleep.

The next morning fog and frost outside were gone, and the icicle had thawed in me. With many thanks and almost tearful gratitude I left, and was home in time to welcome the family, returning from church across the deer park; and then to bed, while the candle-flame twenty feet away at teatime had almost the blasting power of a

Seven-Year Cycle

60-pounder battery firing over my tent at night at German batteries in the Hindenburg Line, in May 1917, while nightingales were singing in Mory Copse.

15

St. Martin's Little Summer

April the first of our last spring in the valley was a harmonious day. In the morning John said he saw a squirrel in the holly tree at the bottom of the garden, called the Swamp, where trout had been reared, and salmon smolts, hatched from eggs sent from the Tay in Scotland, released into the Bray. Loetitia said she heard a willow-wren singing among the honeysuckle bines over the runner, which was full of spring-water from winter's rain; and I had seen, in the gravel shallows of the river, the first salmon-fry of the season.

Gossamers were gleaming in the upper air soon after breakfast. The circumambient air, faintly misty, was a living thing. Midges and other water-flies crossed and floated by the windows; the south wind was melting winter's ice in the heart.

A greenfinch disappeared into the top of the eastern yew tree on the lawn, a dry grass in its beak. Tortoiseshell butterflies were on the rockery aubretias, with bees. I took off the clothes of Robert, now rising four years, and let him run about on the grass, singing with delight. There was a gleam in the sky, in the faces of children and grown-ups alike, on the leaves of holly and box hedge, the budding branches of hazels, bare ash-poles growing over the runner.

I took off coat and shirt, and sat there, feeling the old indoor winter self dissolving as the sun entered through the skin. Closing my eyes, I fancied I could hear the buds of the blossoms breaking in the pear trees on the lime-washed walls of the cottage behind me. There was wind in the upper sky, and upon the high ground of the moor, revealed by mare's-tail streaks of cloud; but none in the valley. For days and weeks and months the tree-tops seen through the casement windows had swayed to the mindless music of the north wind, for weeks hope had been subdued in the valley, while the garden and lower rooms of the cottage had been sunless, the trees on the hill opposite being higher than the sun's low winter curve. Nothing grew, life was suspended. Then one morning the cream-distempered walls of the cottage interior were shyly glowing with light, a bumblebee was buzzing under the thatch, a great-titmouse was vigorously ringing a little handbell in the lichened branches of the apple trees. The sun was burning away in splendour, along the crests of the dark spruces and oaks of the southern horizon.

Was it but fancy, or anthropomorphic sentimentality, to think that Hope had come with the sun to the valley? Hope was surely there, an intangible force in the sunlight, a creative impulse? Daffodils drooping in the borders, bullied for days by the mindless north, lifted up their broken heads to the glaze of the sun. During the winds and the rains they had waited; now all their life, all the stored sunlight, was drawn from their bulbs. With the true shining of the sun green stalks and leaves glistened with renewed hope, and slowly their heads turned to the heavenly fire.

The mindless winds had gone, there was a delicious warm silence in the valley. Far away the cawing of rooks told that they too were rejoicing in the new lease of life. The lease was not signed yet, the winds might return, perhaps with sleet and snow to burn blossom, numb bee, wreck tortoiseshell wing, silence little tinkling bell of Master Tit; but the lease was drafted. It was only a question of time—unless the Gulf Stream suddenly set another way, and the shores and the rivers rebound with ice, the trees split with frozen sap, the flowers die down to the root.

Away with dark thoughts. Within two days spring was rushing in from the Atlantic, voices of willow-wren and chiffchaff were hidden in general birdsong, smouldering wallflowers flamed in dark beauty with Margaret's eyes, aubretia on the rockery and along the borders massed blue flowers for the bees' delight. Those plashes in the lane were dry, the timber-waggon ruts under the limes in the deer park—desolate daily sight for many months as one walked the same way in all weathers—were trodden out by Aberdeen-Angus cattle, as the grass arose once more.

I saw, as I kept still by the warm white southern face of the cottage, a dark flick by one of the many rusty hand-forged nails to which in olden time the pear branches were tied . . . and there clung a lizard, to set the seal upon the lease of summer.

How great the blessing of sun on arms and back and neck! Death seemed but a reabsorption into the sun, beautiful as present thought and feeling. Was not the lizard my relation upon the earth we shared? Did he not share my home, behind a flake of plaster cracked away from the cob wall? We stared at one another. His eye never blinked, his scales glinted with every shifting dry-leaf forward movement. Each motion was a scarcely audible rustle. He was looking for flies, to lance with his thin black tongue. He saw my eyelid quiver, and flicked back into shadow; then he came forth again, to his god the sun.

Soon we would be leaving these familiar rooms and windows and trees; the river, grassy valley, and Cold Pudding.

I have, from my earliest years, been conscious of what, on occasion, seems to be the silent-rushing terror of Time. Suddenly the past rises up; but one cannot re-enter; the picture, projected so intensely upon the air, vanishes. Howsoever one strives in such moments when one would step beyond the motionless rush of Time, one can never get back.

In the small personal sense, I am still startled when I re-enter the ancient sunlight of our valley life, and see the ghosts of the children playing by the summer river, or under the lime trees' rustling leaves. There is no return; and as I am made, and have always been, I long to return. Only in the past has my being a sense of form. I dream backwards into Time, where my little boy is standing by the gate of the early cottage in Ham, and I am planting aubretia in the cracks of the sett-stones, and wondering if the postman will yet again bring me packets of stories returned from editors.

An instant later, and I am lying in hot sunshine by the yew tree at Shallowford, and it is another little boy, naked and with long yellow curls on his shoulders, looking down seriously at me and saying breathlessly, 'I-I-I-I'll tell 'ee suthin'! There ban't no more bullses in the deer park, be 'm? I zeed 'm all go awayawayaway, din' I?'—for Robbie had just run home to tell me that the small Aberdeen-Angus bull and his heifers had left the grazing beside the river. The same child went with us to fetch beech poles from the park, helping the bigger boys and myself to drag them down the hillside, with ropes tied to the axle of an old pair of iron wheels found in the river after a spate—what Windles called our Rolls-Royce. We passed the oak tree and spoke of Cold Pudding; and leaving the wheels in the lane when we went to tea, Robbie came to me and said it was raining, and then, anxiously, 'Your rice (? Royce) pudden will get wet if you leave 'n outside, you knaw!'

And the letter Windles wrote one December evening and posted and the postman gave me back:

> Dearest Father Christmas
>
> When you come on Christmas eve will you leave me a pair of spurs for digging, an apple and a little bag of marbles. And anything else you like
>
> Love from
>
> WINDLES
>
> xxxxxxxxxxxxxx
>
> PS. If I hang up babys boot it is not because I am greedy it will be for my teddy bear
>
> PPS. Please put a hot water bottle in it for teddy

We could not make out at the time what spurs for digging meant; but looking into this book, twenty years after I first transcribed that letter into my MS., I think he must have seen a cowboy film, where huge tin spurs were used and white flour fired from pistols. Otherwise he showed no interest in horses, but only in machines.

And this letter, laboriously tapped out on the keys of my typewriter, during an hour and a half, by another little boy:

> Dear mummy
>
> Is it been snowing up there it is snowing down here i.
>
> Am go-ing to stay home from school today i hath.
>
> A cold thats why iam not go-ing to school.
>
> Windles is go-ing tohaf my milk to.
>
> Day and tomoro i will go the next day and the next day windles is go-ing tohaf my dinner bag to.
>
> Day be-cas windles bagdous not keep the snow out so he has my bag.
>
> Love from john. ten dogs sat in a roe
> the cat came by the bad dogs drofe.
> Her a-way.

John was in demand for stories. Windles used to ask him to tell him stories in bed; so did Robert; so did Father. That was why John wrote a little story about the dogs and the cat, at the end of his letter, to please his mother.

John, so tranquil and self-contained, made decorations for Christmas. For days he cut strips of newspaper, gummed the ends of each strip together and made a chain, two chains, dozens of chains. Windles praised his work,

'Jolly fine, John, I say, a most marvellous performance,' with a heavy wink at me. John was quietly flurried at this unexpected praise from the usually rough elder brother. Robert called them dickerydations.

One of the last things the children and I did was to smash up completely all the excessive, abused and broken mind-disintegrating cheap chain-store toys which had littered the playroom for too many weeks, months, years. We buried pailfuls of them in the swamp. We burned all the trash and wincey prints, the bogus stimulators, with their fake heroes and fake villains, hack-work of shoddy fiction-merchants, and we watched them blazing, and when they were grey and black ash, we threw on copies of old examination papers and opened a bottle of wine and drank to the New World; of course the children joined with me in a toast to our new home. I stayed downstairs when the children went to bed—Loetitia was away—and read John's book. On the morrow I was going across England to see a farm in a near-derelict district of East Anglia.

Here is John's book, almost exactly as written. (Some of the Anglo-Saxon words removed.)

ABOUT MY LIFE

Chapter One

by John Shapcote Williamson

We have one sister and three Brothers and I live at shallow Ford Filligh and my father Does the gardening and we have a gardener. Me Margrate and Windles have a garden to. And Daddy looks after them.

and I like to play trains and there are Four cottages besides ours.

And we have three servenses and a big garden and There lots of nests in the path. And I like Choclate biscuits.

Chapter tow

And we have a river and Daddy has cauthg lots of fish in it. And dad has caught one sea trout and three sarnons. And we liked them as well. We give them lots of food And we are going to bath to-day. And yesterday when we where bathing I found a candle stick. We thought a fish Jumped up I be-gan to make stones Jump acros the water. And then we sat down in the water. And I sat down in the deep.

Chapter three

And when I first went to school I liked It. But now I don't. And I have to stay home. Because I have a hole in my ear drum.

I don't like sums but I like riting. And Im in standard one. The sums are easy and we have cakes some times. I like egg sandwiches.

We say prayers first. And then we must sloot the teacher. I sit be-side charlie Rippon. I go to a village school. And we have Choclate biscuits. And Ginger ones as well. And cheese sandwiches. I don't like them.

Chapter four

Robert is naughty some times. I like playing with him. He has curly hair. He says Moocow. And all sorts of things.

I read to him. He likes birds. He chaces me with sticks, and chucks things about when the room has been cleaned. He cris when he must come out of the bath. I like him best of the family.

But he Pulls up my plants And I smack him on the hands. And I take him around the garden. And Mr. Ridd chaced me with the buckle strap.

Chapter five

When Daddy feeds the fish—we saw the samans. But they Do not eat the food wich daddy throws in. Only the trout eat that. We saw a big trout there to. They are ever so big theres one called Peter. I tasted some fish food but I didn't like it. The fish do like it. I expect you no that.

Daddy shouted to mummy because she cooked the sea trout wrong.

Chapter six

Yesterday I and daddy went out fishing. Daddy caught elleven fish. I stayed up for supper. We had the fishes. Me and Windles giggled very much. When daddy was fishing I had a cartridge I picked some grass. And then put it in the cartidg for Bullits. Daddy saw a salmon. And I played with a thistle. I Best-way stop now for I'm hungry.

Chapter seven

My father is naughty some times. But I like him. He plays with me. Daddy has a trailer which he Carrias behind his car. He carrad sand in it. and wood in it as well. Daddy takes us up to Goerge-ham. In the car. And we may go there for Whitsun. Daddy took us up to the turnel one sunday, But there were no trains running it was Dark with warter coming frew the ruth, Then we went on the diaDuck, high above the deer-Park. we found a Daed Pheasant on the rails. Daddy gave it to Dolly Ridd and Mrs. Ridd cooked it.

Chapter eight

I went to the sunday school out-ing Monday. We had tea first. And then the sports. We had the service last. We sang at the service of course. Daddy gave us eightpence each for the tea. And we didn't have to pay after all. I gave the money back to daddy. We had sweets give us and a orange to. I didn't like the sweets. But I likD the orang. Miss pippercot the teecher said that we must always go to sunday school. But I have eat up all my sweets.

Chapter nine

Windles has a stuffed barn owl. And when I went in by car I

saw others. One was a heron. I found a dead bird in the Roed. And I took the bird home to Daddy and asked him if I could Have it stuffed. But Dad siad I couldn't have it done like that.

Chapter ten

Mummy widles and I went to land cross. And when we went to bed. We said ee-ee. And it is near the railway line. When we heard the wishle we jump out of bed to watch it. In day time Windles and I go up into the packing room to watch the trains their.

Chapter 11

Some times I go to look at the farmers yard. And I see pigs. Chickens there. And there are broody hens. And the bigest pig . . .

[*Censored*]

. . . And keeper tooked to Mrs. Hill a lot about her turkeys And He tooked to Mr. Hill as well. And we stood by watching them.

Chapter 12

Next day we went out splitting wood for winter. And we went up to the viaduct were the oak logs ly. They have been lying there for five years. In one of the logs we found that some dry rot was eating a log. And in another log we found a lizard. And we split the wood with weges. It was raining while we where do-ing that. And Dad was swet. Atie Bass sawd the wood up. And we put the wood in a heap.

Chapter Thirteen

We went out baving again. Dad was learning us to float. But it was to shallow. so I walked up in the deep. And they all came after me. We went in the deep to. To of us jumped about in it. And I played with my candle stick. And then we saw that mummy was going home. And after she was in a thunder stoom came. But dad went on Baving.

Chapter Fourteen

And a long time after that we found out that they were chopping the trees near our house. And on saturday that's when Windles is home from school we always go up there then. And men stiking the Bottom of the tree. Then a crak comes from the tree ever so loud. And after that they have Breakfast. And they have meat sandwiches. I wish I could have one to. so good by till to-morrow.

Chapter 15

In August we went for our holidays. Mage and I went to George-Ham. We went to Miss-Johnson's at the barn. And she has two swings. And no meat in the house onle vegtadles and fruit. I like moton and baked botatos. But Miss-Johnson calls Muton bludy cuops. I like bananas. When in the sun. Daddy and Windles where up in the Hut eat-ing eggs and Bakon and cake. And some times we go to the see-sands. When we went home I Mage adout the rain. When the sun shines thays giges up to the clouds the sun sucks the water up in the clouds and fills them and they burst and we have a storm.

Chapter 16

Mr. Pine is a nice man. He takes Windels out to stage head in the rain. I like him to. He give us jumps us up. My father has gone to garmany to see hitler. We have a new baby called richerd. He is a nice boy. He is not quite 2 monthes old. My mother has to rest to make good milk. He sukcs the milk up until hes had a enuf.

Chapter 17

Saterday it was roberts bithday. He had two litele candels. My sister is a fool. She wores me when im doing my chapter. We had some nice Poem Biscuits. The next day when we where haveing tea I found a candel un-der my sponge-roll. In September we pick our pairs. Their not eit-ing piars atoll.

Chapter 18

My mother has gone to help our uncle to help him to pack. (she took the baby with her.) At the end of September he will be 2 months old. Our uncle is aniceman to. Hes comeing to stay with us next week Im glad. My father is riting a buot a samen.

Im six years old and in october Ill be 7.

Auntybess went in the river to get the eal-trap.

Mrs. Ridd gave to mushrooms the smorning.

Chapter 19

when it was our other babys* bithday we didnt have a partey becois we had one last week. We had races instead I wone in jump-ing and ti-leg so I had 2 prises. our ante gave the prizes. Dolly Ridd wonn five prisses. John Slee won free prises and sodid my brother. We slept in the caravan last nite and so we did we coident go to have brakfast so we had to go home in the rain.

Chapter 20

Robbert went to soth-molton last-niget and came back when we was in bed and fast asleep. Phylliss brother gave robert a wothe and a lillte man. I thinck its a go-ing to rain to day and it may wash our home a-way.

Chapter 21

When they kill pig's they cut it's throit I now it's cruel to do that itnst it.

When they kill sheep they nock them down and cut it in hatf I think thay do.

Their is a tree crashed neir our house. Uncle came with his lugege yester-day and we wiar glad. he has made my sister a dolls houes the best you've ever seen I bet you.

* Rosemary, whose birthday was near to Robert's, shared the party.

Chapter 22

(We are go-ing to barnstable fair to-morrow.)

Chapter 23

When we went to barnstap fair I and my brother went on a thing called the cake-walk and the nowers ark twice. Our uncle took my sister on the dodgers. I did not go in them be-cause I dont like them. We went on the horeses onec. We went on the hellter scellter onec. My mother didn't buy any rock. rock is what I like it's hot. Margaret was the only one to buy any-thing. She bought some sweets. I had one of them. we bought 5 huge balloons with big noses. A man wanted to have a thoto taken. But we would not let him.

Chapter 24

I loved the Fair. Circuses are Better still I love those funny clowns. And once I went to one, and a litlle pony had to jump over a big Horse. But it only ran under it. HA. HA. HA. Well when I did that Ha Ha Ha I didn't raely mean it. I like rite-ing be-caese It makes me lathe.

I like fancy mixed bisciets. To-morrow i must write my last chapter. To-morrow I will be rite-ing some more funny things in my book.

Chapter 25

In January
when I was tak-ing
our two babys down
by the river. We came
to a little bridge by the
saw-mills. I thought I would
go across and get some
saw-dust. Then one
of the babys thuoght that the
water would hold him
so he stepped in. Then with cries

of terror I ran over the bridge and
tried to pull him out at last I managed
to by pulling him to the bank. Then we
started for home I had two carry the baby
over the boggy parts be-cause he had lost
his wellingtons.

Chapter 26

Here we are a-gaen. Today I will write to say that I am very sorry to leave this book.

My father wants to be a farmer. We will be leave-ing Devon soon we dont know where we are go-ing yet. Im go-ing to say good by to all the villige-people. And the silver fish in the river. And the dear old house which has kept us safe. I won't be-adle to write any more of this book be-cause I am going back to school in six and a Half days time.

Daddy is go-ing away. To by a farm. To-night Daddy and I and all the others will have a bottle of shampain.

Loetitia was away on that occasion, and I thought there could be no harm in letting them have a drink for once. So we sat before a fire and wished one another luck. The effect of the wine on each of us was different: Windles, 11, became wild and moody; John, nearly 9, was pugnacious; Margaret, 6, kept up a flow of wit, cheek, and laughter. At times she might have been 25 years old in her sayings.

The effect on me was to open up the various lodes of my mind. Sitting alone in my chair when the children had gone to bed, I meditated how the years lived in Devon had been entwined with personal failure, because so far below the standards I had set my mind to follow. My mistakes with the children glared at me; for example, Margaret, after one small glass, had told me that for years she had believed what I had once said to her in a thoughtless moment, before the boys. *You are dark because I got you from the Zoo, your real father was a monkey, and they let me have you for an experiment, to see how far you could grow like a real human being.* That most foolish remark, forgotten a moment later, had darkened the child's life, she had brooded on it, believing that what I said was true. At times her brothers had reminded her of her mixed nature. *Maggot, you are half a monkey!* Margaret had not spoken to her mother about it, but borne the supposed tragedy of her parenthood alone.

Then there was the case of Windles's romantic love for a tar engine. This object used to live, when not working, beside graded heaps of road metalling on a level space off the main road into Barnstaple. We often passed it in the motor, as black as black, its wheels and upright cylindrical body being entirely coagulated with bitumen, from scores of heatings of that element, and hundreds of pail-dippings for pouring it on the road surface before spreading the granite chippings for the steam-roller to press in. Windles's eyes glowed whenever he saw it; it was alive for him. *It's a darling old tar engine, isn't it, Mum. I wish I could have it to look after it!*

'What, that thing? It's a DIRTY old tar engine, anyone can see that!'

In a rage the four-year-old boy had cried, 'It's a CLEAN old tar engine!'

It became a habit to quip him about that bit of property belonging to the Devon County Council, as we passed it on the road. Many years later, John Middleton Murry, reading the first edition of this book in 1954, asked how I could have persisted in taunting the small boy, after my own experiences with my father. For by that time Windles had left the family, to wander abroad in search of work, and after some vicissitudes had fulfilled what appeared to be a boyhood dream by driving a 50-ton, or it might be a 100-ton, road-grader on new roads through the forests of Canada.

I think that often we tend to grow a spiritual callosity over what was hurt. How often does an adult man exclaim, *I often hear myself saying to my son the very same phrases which as a boy I so disliked in my own father, and criticized so severely, in my mind at any rate, later in youth.*

16

Soliloquy on a Tea-Chest

While waiting for the lorry, driven by a brother of Loetitia's who was coming with us to Norfolk, I sat on a tea-chest filled with books and wrote at a carpenter's bench, noting that the noise of a cat howling through the house was strangely loud; that the walls of the room were bare around me; that pictures, chairs, fishing-rods, books, fire-dogs, lapping crook, the blackened kettle with handy-maid, fire-pick, and bellows of the open hearth were all gone.

The house was almost empty; I was writing a newspaper article, the first of many I hoped would help provide capital to farm the land I had bought with money on a mortgage.

The new home on the north Norfolk coast lay 301 miles away, almost in a direct line as the roads ran E.N.E. from the thatched cottage where my children had started their lives, where my books had been written, where I and my friends had sat and talked and listened to music far into the night. I felt myself to be a proper Fleet Street man, calm in the midst of chaos. For if the farming venture continued as it had begun, at almost right-angular cross purposes, how should we fare upon 240 acres of almost derelict land, with little money and no practical experience? However, despite my literary doubt, I had a store of energy and faith to do what I was about to set out to do.

Slowly the sun moved round the yew tree on the lawn. Some future dweller in the house might find empty bottles of antique shape—early twentieth century—lodged in the wire-bound branches of the tree outside the dining-room window, and wonder how they got there.

One or two of the bottles, sailing through the window, had burst against their fellows; but the midnight shards were always gathered up in the morning, I hastened to add, lest an impression of indifference for the children's bare feet be given to readers of the *Daily Express*.

It wasn't often that bottles flew out of the window: perhaps half a dozen times in nearly eight years. None during the last three, I reassured my readers.

Why was one going to Norfolk? New impressions were required. I felt I was written-out. During the past year, after the salmon book had been published, I had hardly fished in the river. Thousands of hours of watching from tree-branch and pool-side, all the excitement of seeing salmon spawn and otters playing; trout, herons, and kingfishers at their ways—the essence of the years was in print, safe at least from change and decline. Nothing there was left to do, except to repeat oneself.

The cat was still meeowing from one empty room to another. Honey wondered what had happened. Where were the chairs he used to sleep on? Where the dark nooks by which he sat to await mice from the cracks in the wainscoting? Needing reassurance, he came to me with a chirrup and touched my arm with a paw. Yes, I was still there. He was a handsome creature, sensitive and faithful—more like dog than cat—and his coat was the colour of his name.

Most of the cats we had had were black. All became rabbiters in the plantation on Bremridge Hill behind the cottage, growing rough and dishevelled, some with paws foreshortened or spatulate from getting in gin-traps. All disappeared. But Honey was different. He did a bit of hunting, but only as a pastime, so he was still alive.

His basket, lined with hay for the journey, lay on one of the shelves in the empty larder.

Outside the window the leaves of the pear-tree moved slightly in the wind. Wasps droned sleepily at the rinds of hollow pears where blackbirds had ceased to pick. It was a fine sunny September; the corn harvest was over, and Thanksgiving had been held in the parish church.

There was no farmhouse on the land in Norfolk. The arable lay above the premises by the river, so that everything would have to be carried up and down hill. The land was weedy, its fertility gone. Farming that land would give no profit, I was told; I should lose my money. But land had not been so cheap for nearly two centuries; the farming depression, now merged into a business depression, had come near to bottom. One of two things would happen, I believed: either the international money system, by which millions of sterling, francs, or dollars, etc. could be shifted by telephone from one country to another, to depress markets or cause little booms to enrich by speculation, would collapse under new challenges; or its adherents would go to war in an attempt to save the system. In either event farming would be a good thing again.

I wondered how long the dams in the river would last; and if the new tenant, who had come from Singapore, would feed the tame trout in the pool below Humpy Bridge? Or consider them to be cannibals, and get them out with worms?

As for the Canadian willows I had planted in the swamp, pushing slips a foot long and a quarter of an inch thick into yellow clay under the rushes, the tallest was now nearly thirty feet high.

Would the oil-lamps, with their bulbous glass globes seventy years old, on the station platform give way to electric light? They were friendly lamps to me. Many times I travelled home by night on the slow line from Taunton, coming from Bristol and the B.B.C. Studios in Whiteladies Road, after going there by the morning train. Sometimes it was a rush to get to Temple Meads station by 7.10 p.m., but not when I was talking on the Children's Hour in the late afternoon.

Once I had to give two talks in the one December day, the first at 5.15 p.m. and the other at 8 p.m. The morning train left Filleigh station at 11.6 a.m., and calling in at the post office on my way to the station, I found a telegram telling me that the 8 p.m. broadcast was cancelled. This was at the time of the abdication of Edward VIII, and I thought to try and get through by telephone to ask if the earlier talk to children was cancelled also. But there was delay; and when I heard the train coming through the cutting, I dropped the receiver and ran to the station, jumping in just in time. Arriving at the studio for the 4.30 p.m. rehearsal, I found that the talk also was cancelled. So I went to the cinema, and walked down to Temple Meads later on for the 7.10, sorrowing a little that the Prince of Wales, whom I had first seen in Belgium in 1914, and who was popular with officers and men alike, should be in such trouble.

I had a carriage to myself. The train rushed into the night of the Somerset willow moors, while I tried to absorb information from *The Farmer & Stock-Breeder*. At Taunton I got out and there was ten minutes to wait for the 8.20 home. I got a cup of tea from the small stall by No. 3 platform, and was sipping its cabbage-like flavour when I saw the train moving out. So I yelled and ran after it and it stopped; it left at 8.15 and not 8.20 as I had supposed.

Still a little subdued by the spectre of homelessness which had never entirely left me since 1914, I sought an empty carriage of the type then happily in use, with but one length of seat. Then I switched off the light, and lay back, hat over eyes to shut the reflections away on the window-glass of people talking in the next carriage.

A night journey home in darkness was always enjoyable, in a secret sort of way. I had done it about a dozen times during that winter. I played a game with myself, trying to remember the number of station stops, and to switch on my light only when the train had passed through the tunnel leading to the viaduct over the river, and its unmistakable hollow roar upon the steel framework of that high place. It was a game of patience, with hazards of dropping asleep, passing my station, and having to walk back from Barnstaple, weary and my supper missed.

Usually I forgot how many stations there were down the line from Taunton. At every one the train stopped to the waving of an oil-lantern, gruff voices, perhaps the moving of a box, or a calf, a passenger alighting, before on again, puffing into darkness. There were also two stops at halts.

On this December journey, lying back with shut eyes, I tried to get them in right order. Norton Fitzwarren, Milverton, Wiveliscombe pronounced Willscumb, I knew that order: then was it East Anstey, Molland, Molland Junction, Dulverton; or did West Anstey come after Morchard Road? I must work it out without looking at a time-table or peering through the window after rubbing away steam-vapour. But I allowed myself the inverted reflection of a station name in the opposite window provided I was lying down. To read this the near window must be down, as a steam layer covered the outside glass.

It was cold with the window down, so I pulled it up on the strap, while seeing stars flashing in frost. Steam-heat soon fogged the outside glass. Then by the sudden increase of noise coming through the floor I knew we were running on the length of experimental steel sleepers. By now my thoughts were with the King, and his great loneliness. Would he soon be making his last journey to the coast, and so away for ever from the land that would seldom leave his thoughts, which were his life, for his life was England? And I wondered if I would be home in time to hear his farewell on the wireless. Sometimes the train ran late. But now that my brother-in-law had come home from half-way round the earth to start the farm with me, he would be at the station with my motor. The train journey from Taunton was about forty miles, and usually it took an hour and a half. The broadcast was to be at 10 p.m.

I lay back, pulled hat over eyes, determined to lie there until I heard the sudden hollow wheel-roar which meant we were come upon the viaduct. But I could not endure the idea of missing the King, and at a station got up, opened the window, and found we were at South Molton, the station before my own. Then we were puffing on again; the whistle screamed as we entered the tunnel and then we were through, the tops of the spruces were getting lower and lower, stars were increasing; we were in space, the hollow duskiness of meadows lay far below, with the blue glimmer of the winter river and its pools.

Now I could switch on the light and blink back into the ordinary world once more. It was 9.52 p.m. We were late. On the platform with the silhouette of sombre rhododendrons, the solitary porter took the ticket of the one passenger to get off in the light of one bulbous oil-lamp; while the engine, as though eager for its home-yard, was snorting dragon breath into the western sky. There was the open car in the yard, a figure moving towards me, and we were going over the bridge and up the short hill by the beeches and down the hill past the Spanish chestnuts beyond the deer-park railings, white-misted river and candle-lit cottage. It was two minutes of ten o'clock when I got indoors, to find a beech fire on the hearth, my eldest son curled up in pyjamas next to his mother, and a bowl of hot soup awaiting me. But who could eat while the soft scratching of the loudspeaker was about to break into fatal words?

'This is Windsor Castle. His Royal Highness Prince Edward.'

Would H.R.H. break down? After five words he paused, like a man trying to speak without oxygen on a Himalayan peak; but he would not break down. Old soldiers only fade away.

Soliloquy on a Tea-chest

How quickly the events of one's life pass! Sitting on the three-ply wooden cube of books, I am peering at salmon in the Fireplay pool below the viaduct, which often in the dusky summer nights, as I lay beside the water, pleasantly tired after trouting, gleamed with fire as the engines drew the trains across the sky under a rosy glow of steam. And the ice-sheets at the water's edge in January, when the yellow-fungoid kelts, the spawned-out salmon, were locked in the pool, dying because the time of going down to the sea, to clean themselves as fishermen say, was past; for no rain had come to bear them down. So they lay in ruin, or slowly moved about the confined pool, not always evenly, but sometimes heeling over in what seemed to me to be delirium.

Now I am on the viaduct with the children, it is summer, we lean over the low criss-cross fence of iron to the south, launching paper gliders into the warm wind. One is by chance just balanced for the warm air arising from the metalling of the land below, and floats almost level for nearly five minutes. Did we recover our white ships made from sheets of newspaper, did we pick them up lest they litter his Lordship's deer park? I was always fussy about tidiness, so probably we recovered them, and took them home. But who is this on an all-nickel-plated motor-cycle with an immense engine of two cylinders and ten horse-power, this shy young man with a very red face and gold hair and the quietest, merriest laugh in the world? Can it be—Lawrence of Arabia come to see us after all? A graft of gold leaves upon the tree of my life. *So explicit a man.* That was his post-script in a letter written from Fort Wahiristan, about C. M. Doughty, who had just died.

Another friend, who loved trains, once drove a chocolate-and-yellow Great Western engine from Paddington when he came to visit us. He said that regular drivers upon any route knew where they were at any part of the journey by echo; each bridge, gradient, cutting, fenced-in or hedged field or wood, and of course every tunnel, had its own resonance. We went for a walk on the viaduct with the children, and went on into the tunnel lying to the east, a great cavernous place of jagged blasted rock dripping with water, a vast darkness briefly spotted at each end by a pin-head of light. I feared for the children while trusting John Heygate to know the whereabouts of every train anywhere in Great Britain at any given moment. He certainly knew about this tunnel, which might have been reserved for our promenade; a not so very mysterious knowledge when one learned that he had inquired of trains, both up and down, at Filleigh station beforehand.

O, so much and so much in memory! Must all that life be lost? A piercing moment, which comes to every man on occasion: a poignant wish to bring back lost time, to make the dead to live, to smile again in the immortal sunshine of one's life. We are pierced; and we are helpless: until we realize that we are born to be vehicles of grace, by which alone a man can truly live.

An empty house; already a house of ghosts. Furniture gone, children gone, a late bee buzzing about the room; Honey the cat walking disconsolately, slowly, up the bare stairs; the calm sunshine of St. Martin's Little Summer filling the valley.

There's a bat hanging, folded and head down, in what was the night nursery.

He thinks he's found a quiet place for his winter sleep.

Ah, there's the lorry, rounding the corner by the lane,

come for the last of the garden tools and the junk I've not been strong-minded enough to leave behind.

For more than a year I've been looking forward to this moment—going far away to a new life, a natural life of body-working after the strains of imaginative quiescence.

Now the moment has come; and ghosts are crying all around—the ghosts that live and die with a man's memory.

Come on, cat, into your basket! Pack up pen and paper. Leave the key in the door for the new tenant. One last look round. Good-bye, little house—forgive my occasional harsh words, thank you for sheltering us—good-bye, Shallowford, good-bye.

Epigraph

Now for a brief note of how we got on, after we had left Shallowford.

Some of our adventures are recorded in *The Story of a Norfolk Farm*, an account which ended, through necessity, in 1940; and since then, more than one reader has inquired: What has happened to the children?

I write this in the summer of 1958. The eldest boy flew to Canada in 1947, where he has remained. He is married, with two children, and lives in a house with all modern gadgets. Loetitia went to visit him last year, thus making real some of the exile's thoughts of England. Margaret has seen him, too, for she goes to Canada periodically with her husband.

The second boy John, after some years at a boarding-school in Norfolk where Admiral Horatio Nelson was considered to be the most distinguished Old Boy, joined the R.A.F. as an aircraftman, second grade. However he managed to rise to 29,700 feet in an old glider and win the De Haviland Cup for breaking the height record. But I must not trespass upon the territory of his younger brother Richard, who also went into the R.A.F. as an erk and while there wrote a book entitled *The Dawn is My Brother* which is to be published soon. So, for that and other reasons, this is my last book on the family, although some members may play bit-parts in novels later on, if I am 'lived and spared', as Jimmy the stockman on the Norfolk farm used to say.

We had a mixed time on the farm at first. I had to write half the night, after a heavy day of physical work, in order to get money to pay the wages and other outgoings. There was no money for education, for when the war came all the pre-war forms of journalism, broadcasting and book publishing stopped. Dark days, physically and spiritually, followed; but later the farmer could sit down and write, and so, metaphorically speaking, get on his feet again.

Then, with something coming in, as they say in Norfolk, Margaret went to her mother's old school at Wantage in Berkshire, after periods at various other schools; afterwards she learned to cook at the Cordon Bleu, and married her young painter who has a studio-attic off the Fulham Road.

The farm was sold, after eight years, at a price which returned the reconstruction work on it—the draining and bridging of meadows, making of roads, cottages, etc. This permitted the two younger boys to be sent to a school in Devon, where one of the Old Boys is a character in fiction, John Ridd, who married Lorna Doone. On being also rid of the classroom, Robert joined the R.A.F., also as an AC2, rose to AC1, and then retired to enter industry as other men have done after the end of their service. Robert is now in Canada with an electronic company. There he married and remains a happy young man. Robbie is especially dear to me, because he resembles in face and figure my own father, with whom in life I was almost estranged.

There is another child, born in the last year of the war, named Sarah, who has become quite a horsewoman.

The chronicler is back where he started as writer, in Devon; indeed, he writes this in the hut, now thoroughly waterproof; while the family is based on a Suffolk cottage. There, at times, we are together under the matriarchal eye of Loetitia, who amidst other work manages to tidy up the cottages of and to cook for several old people in the town of Bungay. Through her stability and equal-mindedness some hopes of youth have materialized.

1937–1958,
Norfolk–Devon.

Afterword

Another twenty years have passed since Henry wrote his Epigraph, and it is with sadness that I now find myself taking his place to write this Afterword. For Henry died on 13 August 1977 at the age of 81, in a nursing home cared for by the Alexian monks, on the very day that the death scene for the film of *Tarka the Otter* was shot in Devon on the river Torridge. A few days later the children of Shallowford came to Devon and for the first time since the family had left forty years previously, were all, with their mother, gathered together in the one place which their father knew as home, his hilltop field at Georgeham, some twenty miles from Shallowford. Henry was buried in Georgeham churchyard, next to the church tower where he often gleefully pulled the bell ropes when nobody was about, and within a few yards of the cottage where he began his writing career in 1921.

The eldest son, Windles, had flown from Canada immediately upon hearing the news. Fortunately, he was not at that time in the far north of the country where his work, in charge of highway construction, frequently takes him. His wife and four children were unable to accompany him.

The second boy John, working at a desk job at Farnborough on electronic installations for the R.A.F. Tornado fighter, came with his Swedish wife and two children from his home in Surrey. Gliding remains his passion and he has won the British Championship and represented this country several times in the World Championships. The third child, Margaret, now supervising paperwork in a large London hospital, came from her home in Barnes. She it was who visited Henry constantly in his last months in the London nursing home where he lived before his death. Her former husband, 'the young painter', now an established artist, was there too as one of the pall bearers.

Robert, the fourth child, came from Essex with his wife and child, where he is now the headmaster of a primary school, a job which he loves. Dealing with people rather than objects gave his spirit more freedom. His daughter is a keen horse-woman. As for myself, next in line; well, shall we say that I now know how Henry must have worked to keep us all in the war when he worked by day on his Norfolk farm and wrote at night to make it pay. My job as warden of a National Nature Reserve in Sussex leaves little energy for my writing life, but I have managed another book, about a roebuck called *Capreol*, and a third about my reserve, called *The Great Yew Forest*, while I hope to start on Henry's biography soon, and have many more books planned. My wife helps me with running the literary side of Henry's estate, and we've added two more children to the Williamson tribe.

Sarah, born in Norfolk, and thus not one of the Shallowford children, lives and works in California, loving the land of such beauty and warmth. It is one of her mother's greatest pleasures to be able occasionally to visit her there and travel the western seaboard with her 'baby', afterwards crossing the Rockies by train to be with her firstborn.

One more son was born to Henry, by his second wife Christine. At the present time Harry is living at the Georgeham field in the large white house which Henry had built in the last years of his life. He has recently produced some striking and evocative orchestral music which, he says, was inspired by *Tarka*. We await more of his talent with keen interest.

We all, in one way or another, played 'bit-parts' in the books which Henry continued to write after the Epigraph of 1958. He was at that time deeply committed to the *Chronicle of Ancient Sunlight*, a series of novels encompassing not only his own life but the social history of the period through which he lived, including the two great wars. Nine of these novels, or nearly two million words, followed in the last nineteen years of his life; not to speak of many newspaper articles, a book about a pigeon called *The Scandaroon*, some television films, and a massive film treatment for *Tarka*. Writing kept him alive and well, and he simply finished all that he had set out to do, which was a great achievement, and thus in one sense he was happy at the end. When the writing was finished, the vital spark went out of him, although the strong physical body struggled a little longer.

How stands his talent in the world? Henry's mortal mind felt aggrieved that little recognition of his talent came within his life. But more and more people are discovering, will discover, that his particular brand of magic is unique, that no other writer so completely explains those moments of joy or sadness which even slightly imaginative people experience when absorbed within the natural world. As children we experienced this at first hand. Our informative years, that period of Time Lost so well known to the human race, was more than unusually explored by the father who had been there once himself, and who through the craft of his trade knew how to return. The pity was that for some of us more than others, the moments were rare. The children who left Shallowford experienced an abrupt change in their lives, particularly the eldest. But whatever happened in those dark war days could not eradicate the joys of earlier years; the days of watching salmon under the bridge, of helping father dam the river, of the stories about Cold Pud, of the Christmas nights in the Deer Park.

Already some of the grandchildren have been back to bathe in the pool below the bridge, to look (at a distance, so as not to disturb the new owner) at the house and wonder at the far away days.

RICHARD WILLIAMSON
May 1978